McGowen, Tom
Sir Machinery; illus. by Trina Schart Hyman. Follett Pub. Co. [c1970]
155 p. illus.

Sir MacHinery

Sir Machinery

TOM McGOWEN

ILLUSTRATED BY TRINA SCHART HYMAN

FOLLETT PUBLISHING COMPANY
CHICAGO

ISBN 0-695-40167-X Titan binding
ISBN 0-695-80167-8 Trade binding

Library of Congress Catalog Card Number: 78-118965

First Printing

To my son,

ALAN,

who taught me the true meaning of science,

and to my daughter,

GAYLE,

who shares my fondness for fantasy.

Sir Machinery

Chapter 1

In the northern part of Scotland, past the valley that is known as the Great Glen, the land sweeps away toward the sea in wild and wonderful desolation. Here are the oldest mountains in Europe—grim, gray, towering cliffs, crags, and crannies with names such as Canisp, Suilven, and Stac Polly. On their slopes, twisted trees lean against the wind, and great clumps of gorse bush shudder at the onslaught of the gales that rush down from the Arctic Circle. In the few flat places are patches of forest where black green pine trees have grown uncut and unvisited for a thousand years and more. For the people in this region are few, and few they have been since the very beginning of things.

All of Scotland is well steeped in legend, but this bit of land is thick with strange tales. Here, it is said, is the abode of the wee, dark people, and of the green men and the seal folk, as well as of brownies and animals most strange to see. There are glades in the woods on the mountainsides where the devil himself comes to dance with witches on All Hallow's E'en. There are rings of black boulders called cromlechs, and piles of black stones called cairns, and it is wise to avoid both after sundown. Giants walk in these parts, too, and their huge footprints have been seen in patches of snow by many sober and serious men. There are any number of old and ruined abbeys, castles, and cottages filled with ghosts, moanings, groanings, and clanking of chains.

Probably the least haunted and most modern of all the castles in the area was the one which squatted at the top of a small hill called Auld Clootie, which rose above the tiny village of Strathgow. The castle had been built in the sixteenth century and was the ancestral home of the Earls of Strathgow, who had lived in it until well into modern times. But earls, like kings, dukes and noblemen of all ranks, had gone out of fashion by the early days of the twentieth century, and most of them had to give up their old castles and manor houses to go out into the world to find jobs. The last Earl of Strathgow had left Scotland in 1936, and the castle had stood deserted, and presumably haunted, ever since. Until the strange American millionaire rented it.

He wasn't really a millionaire but he was an American, and to the people of Strathgow that was the same thing. He came bumping up the old road into town in an American automobile that was the biggest car ever seen in that part of Scotland. The seats and trunk of the car were filled with boxes marked FRAGILE and MACHINERY. He stopped the first villager he happened to encounter, Mr. Darling, the tavern keeper, and asked the whereabouts of the chief of police. Mr. Darling and the large crowd which had collected finally decided that he meant the chief constable, so they took him to the home of Jock Wier, the town constable and sole law officer. The American introduced himself as Simon Smith and showed Constable Wier some papers which proved that he had rented Strathgow castle and was entitled to live in it. Then he drove on up the old cart road that wound to the top of Auld Clootie.

In the following weeks, trucks from such far-off places as Glasgow and Edinburgh drove into the town and up to the castle. Like Simon Smith's automobile, these trucks were piled high with large and small wooden boxes, through the slats of which the peering villagers could see gleams of glass and glints of metal. And the people of Strathgow began to wonder what all these boxes of machinery might be for, and why a rich American would want to seclude himself in an old, uncomfortable, presumably haunted castle. In a village where practically nothing exciting ever happened, this became a mammoth mystery.

It was the chief topic of conversation among the men who met at Mr. Darling's pub each evening. Hunched over tankards of beer, they frowned in concentration, trying to arrive at a logical but suitably interesting conclusion. Finally, Mr. Darling was able to shed some light on the matter. He told how a search for his lost dog had led him to the castle on a previous evening. Mr. Darling's dog was twelve years old and never left his sleeping place beside the fire, but by silent, mutual consent, the listening men did not bring up this point. Thinking that the dog might have wandered into the castle, said Mr. Darling, but not wishing to disturb Mr. Smith, he had found a lighted window and peered into it. This had not been very easy, as the window was some ten feet above ground level and Mr. Darling had had to climb up a drainpipe to reach it. He had seen a large room, littered with open and empty wooden boxes. In the center of the room stood a massive table upon which lay a glittering apparatus, and over this Simon Smith had been hunched in feverish concentration. There had been no sign of the dog, Mr. Darling hastened to add.

At this point, Mr. Edward Small, a retired Sergeant Major of a famous Scottish regiment spoke up. "I passed there the other night, too, and I heard a most curious noise. A buzzing like, it was."

The men considered these items of information thoughtfully. "Och, he must be a scientist," Mr. McMurdoch the butcher announced with awe. "He's inventing something up there."

" 'Tis a monster he's making," declared old Ritchie McMullin, who was fond of American horror movies. "You wait. It'll be comin' doon from the castle any night now, seven feet tall, wi' a great, green face and a thirst for human blood!" He shivered happily and dunked his walruslike mustache into a tankard of ale.

Actually, both Mr. McMurdoch and old Ritchie were pretty close to being right. Simon Smith was a physicist, which is one kind of scientist, and he was making a sort of monster. But it wasn't seven feet tall with a great, green face—it was exactly three feet two inches tall and it was silver, all over. It was a robot.

The dictionary says that a robot is "a machine in the form of a human being that performs the mechanical functions of a human being but lacks emotions and sensitivity." But that is not the most complete explanation. Any number of machines designed to do various kinds of work could be put into manlike bodies, but they would not really be robots. A real robot would be a machine that could think just as a human being does. It would be a machine with a brain and the ability to act as the brain directed it—almost a *live* machine.

And this was precisely what Simon Smith had made. The robot was little because Simon had wished to conserve on expensive materials, but was quite manlike in appearance, with a round head, body, arms and legs, and hands and feet. Inside the squat metal tube that served as the body was an incredibly complicated mechanism, the basis of which was a small, compact analytical computor.

From this, a network of fine wires ran, like a nervous system, to all parts of the body. Tiny, twin television scanning lenses peeped out of the round head and sent images down to the computor memory bank. This brain evaluated the images and sent messages to the movable portions of the body, telling them what to do. All of this took less than a millionth of a second. On each side of the head were slotted grills behind which were sensitive microphones serving as ears. And on the front of the globe, below the eye lenses was another grill with a miniature radio speaker connected to the device through which the robot could talk.

The little robot was the result of many years of hard work by Simon Smith, who had come to northern Scotland to find complete privacy for the final stages of its construction. And it so happened, on that very night while Mr. Darling, Old Richie, and the other men had been discussing Simon Smith and his mysterious doings, the robot's construction was finished. The last solenoid circuit had been wired in, the last screw tightened, and the last seam soldered. The robot was ready to be brought to life.

Simon Smith was most excited. He brought the robot into what had once been the main dining hall of the castle, a huge, high-ceilinged room with a single great window. The centuries-old table and chairs still stood in the center of the room. Dragging one of the chairs away from the table, Simon set the robot carefully upon it. He gazed fondly at his wonderful creation and dreamed of the fame and fortune that would be his when he had tested his model robot and could offer it to the world.

"Gosh, I'm tired," he exclaimed, yawning and rubbing his eyes. "I've been working so hard to get you finished that I haven't been to bed for almost forty-eight hours." He yawned again. "I'd love to start those tests right now, but I just don't think I can stay awake a minute more. I'll get a good night's sleep and when I'm fresh again, I'll give you a good workout."

Shuffling about the huge room he blew out the tall, thick candles, which were his only source of light in the old castle. Then he returned to the table and picked up the massive, pewter candelabra. Holding this high, he let the yellow radiance flicker upon the robot's gleaming body. Then, with another jaw-stretching yawn, he turned and trudged to the door at the far end of the room. It squeaked shrilly as he opened it, squeaked again as it thudded shut behind him. And with the second squeak, the room plunged into inky darkness.

Time passed. The full moon rose in the night sky, and a thin shaft of silver light spilled its soft brilliance over the small metal shape. But then there was a sound. Off in one dark corner there was a faint pattering upon the flagstone floor. Into the flood of moonlight, trotted three tiny men, each no more than twelve inches tall. Ranging themselves in a row in front of the old, carved chair, they stared solemnly up at the silent, shining figure of the small robot.

Chapter 2

For almost a full minute they stood, silently staring up at the seated figure. Despite their tiny size, they were perfectly formed and proportioned—although perhaps a trifle chubby about their middles. Their chins were bearded, and they wore short, brown cloaks with tall, pointed hoods and doublets. Each of them wore a tiny kilt, the plaid of which was worked out in shades of brown and green. Their feet were shod in high boots of soft, brown leather.

At last one of them broke the silence. "Och, he doesna look verra big," he observed in a hoarse whisper.

The tallest of the three, whose sandy-red beard was heavily streaked with gray, shook his head impatiently. "It canna be helped," he whispered sharply. "He's the only knight that's been seen in these parts for hundreds o' years."

"How do ye know he's a knight?" wondered the third little man.

"Because he's wearing shining armor, you ninny," he hissed. "That's how knights look. They wear metal over all their body to protect them in battle. My grandsire told me of this. Knights were common in his time."

The other little man had tiptoed over to one of the boxes littering the room, which had contained apparatus for the robot's interior. Simon Smith had ripped away several of the wooden slats, but on one of those remaining the word MACHINERY was stenciled in bold, black letters. "What does that say, Angus?" called the little man.

The gray-bearded one approached the box. "Like as not 'tis his name," he whispered. Squinting, he brought his eyes close to the letters, and his lips worked silently as he painfully spelled out the word. Old Angus, who was an uncertain speller at best, got off on the wrong foot. "Mac—Hinn—eree," he read, slowly. "Aye, that's it—MacHinery. It's a good Scottish name, though I'm not familiar wi' the clan."

They all turned back to the robot. "Still asleep," old Angus commented. "Ye've the strongest lungs, Gowrie, give him a yell."

Gowrie put his hands up beside his mouth and shouted, "Waken, Sir MacHinery!" The robot, of course, did not stir.

"Och, he's a sound sleeper," Angus said. "Come on lads, let's all call together." They did so, with no better result.

"Perchance he canna hear us through that steel pot he's wearing," Gowrie suggested. "Pound his shins, Angus."

"That'll but bruise my knuckles and perchance make him angry," growled Angus. "I think there's naught for it but to climb up where we can open his visor and yell in his ear. Let's be at it."

The other two clasped their hands together to form a sort of platform and with a heave, they lifted Angus up to where he could grasp the arm of the chair. "Fwooshed if I know why he sleeps wi' his armor on anyway," he grumbled, pulling himself up.

"Perchance he's afeared of the crazy foreigner that's livin' in the castle," called Gowrie in a loud whisper.

"Ah, there's naught to be afeared of from him," replied Angus. He was standing on the chair arm now, and leaning forward with one hand on the robot's shoulder. "The foreigner is a colonial and they be a queer lot, but they're not dangerous. Now if I can find out how this helmet comes apart . . ." He groped with his hand on the robot's head and by pure chance came down upon the very button that would activate the robot, and pressed it.

The ear microphone on the left side of his head picked up a faint noise, and his round head with its twin lens eyes automatically swiveled about.

Although a newborn babe is quite weak and helpless, both physically and mentally, quite the opposite was true of the small robot. His memory bank contained as many facts, figures, and bits of information as a well-stocked library. Furthermore, he knew exactly what he was and how he had come to be. His infrared sensitive eyes could see as well in the dark as in the brightest daylight. And when they opened up upon the gray, stony wall of the castle, the robot knew exactly what kind of stone it was, how long it had been quarried, and the chemical composition of the mortar that held it together.

When he saw a twelve-inch tall man standing upon the chair arm, near his elbow, his computor flashed the impression of a man standing far enough away so as to appear small. But it instantly canceled this out as illogical because the figure was standing upon the arm of a chair, and replaced it with the impression of a miniature human being. Since the tapes that Simon Smith had fed into the robot's computor had not included any information about brownies, the robot regarded the small figure as being a child. He was programmed to treat children with extreme gentleness and to look after their well-being.

"Good evening, my little man," said his vocal apparatus, fed by electronic impulse suggestions from a fifty-thousand word vocabulary section of memory bank. "Is it not well past your bedtime?" His voice, reproduced mechanically, was a flat monotone.

Old Angus was a bit taken aback by both the words and the sound of the voice. His people, the brownies, had not revealed themselves to a human being in several hundred years, and he had fully expected anything from a stunned silence to a shout of surprise. He was really rather crestfallen at the robot's matter-of-fact attitude.

"Aye, it is a bit late, Sir MacHinery," he acknowledged, "but we have verra important matters to talk of with ye, which is why we've waked ye up. There's great trouble coming to the world and ye must help to fight it!"

The robot was silent for a time. His computor brain was sorting out and analyzing the information it had just received. Not having been programmed to deal with brownies seeking help to avert doom, it found itself with too many missing factors for proper analysis.

"I require further information," intoned the robot.

Now it was the brownie's turn to be silent while his brain analyzed the remarks of this strange sounding, small knight. "Ah," he exclaimed at last. "Ye mean ye dinna understand! I'll explain." He sat down on the arm of the chair, his legs dangling. The robot tilted it's head so that the eye lenses continued to stare down at him.

"I don't know much aboot the outside world these days, Sir MacHinery," he began, "but I've heard that mortal men ha' forgotten the old ways and if that be so, I'd best tell ye a few things.

"A very long time ago, when the world was filled with great open places, all the folk of the world lived together in friendship. There were the tribes of men who farmed the fields and hunted. There were the dwarves who lived in the caverns below the earth and loved to make beautiful things from the very rocks of earth. There were the elves who delighted in the cool, green shadows of the forests and who lived in the thickest groves of the deepest woods. And there were my people, the brownies, who were wanderers, going where they pleased and earning their food by performing tasks for others.

"Och, those were the days of bright, open sky and broad, open plains; of great, proud forests, and mountains that stretched up to touch the clouds. There was no smoke clotting the air then, and the streams that tumbled down from the high places and rushed, laughing through the glades were clean and silver and sparkling! Those were days when a man or an elf or a brownie could walk under the sweeping sky with the golden grass tassels swishing about his legs and the soft wind at his back and shout in a great voice for the very joy of being alive.

"It was a time of great magic, too. There was magic in rocks, trees, air, earth, water, and fire, for those who cared to seek it out. Most did not, but some did. And that was how the trouble began. For as any creature who lives upon this world well knows, where there is love of life and love of the good power that gives life, great evil will always grow and try to become master.

"For then, a dwarf from one of the greatest of all the dwarf tribes, who sought more and more knowledge of magic, came at last upon that great, hungering power of evil that exists to enslave souls, and delights in grief and the spoiling of beauty. The dwarf-sorcerer was ensnared by that power and he in turn ensnared others, until that great tribe of dwarves became possessed by the desire to conquer and enslave and rule. They grew proud and arrogant and cruel. Their once pleasant faces twisted into snarling masks, and their once stalwart bodies blackened and shriveled. They became what all the world called them then and since—*demons.*

"And a war began—the first war of the world. The demons spewed up out of their holes in the ground and swept across the fair earth, and men, brownies, elves, and dwarves banded together to fight them. The air grew foul with the smoke of burning, the streams were filled with poison, and the grass was trampled by the tread of marching armies. And on both sides were wizards, using terrible magical weapons.

"Full centuries that war lasted, Sir MacHinery, with battles raging across the world, with men and brownies being born, growing up and dying and never knowing what it meant to be at peace. But at last, as all things must, the war ended. The evil sorcerer was slain by a great hero of the elf-folk and much of his hideous magical knowledge was lost with him. Without his help the demons were slowly beaten back, and finally they were being harried and hunted like rats. A few of them escaped the avenging swords and axes of their enemies and hid themselves deep in the darkest places of the earth.

"And, yea, though they had lost, the demons in a way had really won. For they had destroyed the old ways forever. Men now began to gather together in villages for protection, while the elves retreated deep into their forests and the dwarves burrowed deeper into the ground. Less and less did they come together, and at last, among men anyway, the memory of elf and dwarf and brownie and demon faded into legend. Each went their way. But we brownies have tried to stay close to all, while still holding to the open places we love. We bide near the tiny towns of men, which lie at the foot of great mountains or on the edge of open moorlands or on the outskirts of the old forests. We keep in touch with the elves in their leafy dwellings and the dwarves in their burrows. And we make ourselves known to those few men who still love and seek the old ways."

Old Angus stopped speaking and glanced up at the great window. The shaft of moonlight had crept its course, and the chair and its metal occupant were half in shadows once again. The brownie hopped down from his perch on the chair arm and stood, legs apart, on the seat beside the robot's metal hip. "It was well that we did this, Sir MacHinery," he stated, "for we have found that the demons have once again grown in strength. They have relearned their ancient magic, and in the thousands upon thousands o' years since they were vanquished, they have made careful plans." He took a deep breath. "I know that the men o' today have armies o' millions. I know they have weapons wi' which they could split the whole world if they chose. The demons know this too. They are cunning.

They know well how to corrupt men. They will turn the nations o' the world against one another. They will offer themselves and their magic to the side they deem strongest. And a war will come that will make other war ages seem like a snowball fight between little boys!"

He shuddered. "I have seen the vision o' what might come. A world in everlasting darkness, where the sun shines not and the towns and cities are but ash heaps. And when the few men left have exhausted themselves and their weapons, the demons will spew forth wi' all their armies and magic and conquer all that is left. And I tell ye Sir MacHinery, so terrible will be their rule that only the dead will be happy."

Chapter 3

Once again the room was filled with silence so complete that the faint whirring of the robot's electronic parts could be clearly heard. His computor memory bank brain was quickly sorting and analyzing the information he had just received. At last he said, "What is required of me?"

"Well, Sir MacHinery," said the old brownie, wagging his head from side to side, "we canna do much ourselves, for there be terrible dangers to overcome and feats of strength to be done. For many and many a month we have been looking for a warrior knight such as you who could help us. Ye must help us, Sir MacHinery! There's much work to do!"

It was fortunate that Angus used the word *work,* for the little robot had been programmed to be ready to do any sort of work required of him. Pushing himself forward, he slid from the chair and set both metal feet on the flagstone floor with a clank that made the brownies wince. "I am at your service," he announced.

Angus hurriedly clambered down from the chair.

"Bless ye, Sir Knight," he panted. "We'll take ye to Maggie MacMurdoch straight off. She'll tell ye what must be done first."

He scuttled toward the door at the far end of the room, the other two brownies trotting after him, and the robot marching along behind at a measured and mechanical pace. At the door, Angus stopped and looked expectantly up at the robot. "Ye'll have to open it, Sir MacHinery," he said, apologetically. " 'Tis too heavy for us."

The robot seized the massive knob, pulled, and the door squealed as it opened. Upstairs, Simon Smith stirred in his sleep and turned over, but did not waken. Followed by the robot, the brownies slipped through the door, hurried down a narrow hall, passed through an archway, and scampered down a short flight of steps and across a broad room to another, larger door. This time, the robot needed no instructions. He pulled the door open, followed the brownies through it, and found himself standing outside the old castle beneath a blue black night sky sprinkled with twinkling stars. Moonlight washed the whole hilltop and dripped down the hillside, spreading out upon the rooftops of sleeping Strathgow far below. Angus and the other two brownies were moving toward the opposite side of the hill which dipped down into a patch of pine forest, out of which rose a gently sloping mountainside. "Hurry, Sir MacHinery," called Angus in a hoarse whisper.

At the forest's edge, the brownies paused and clustered together for a moment. There was a faint scraping sound, and then with a sputter, a flare of fire appeared in old Angus' hand. It was a length of tree branch smeared with pine sap which the brownies had set afire with an old-fashioned flint and steel. Holding this torch to guide the others, Angus plunged into the woods.

The forest eventually gave way to a rock-cluttered clearing out of which slanted a spur of the mountain. The flickering torch fluttered to a stop. The robot saw that he was standing before the mouth of a cave. Raising his voice, the old brownie called, "Maggie! Come oot! We've found one at last!"

Almost immediately two shapes materialized out of the pitch-black darkness of the cave, both clearly visible to the robot's vision. One was an old woman with an extremely wrinkled but pleasant face crowned with a mop of white hair. The other was a large, tan cat with a tail bent into the shape of a corkscrew. It stalked majestically along at the old woman's side.

"Sir MacHinery, this be Maggie MacMurdoch," announced old Angus, and then added, "She's a good witch."

The old woman hobbled forward and peered down at the robot, for although she was a small person herself, she towered head and shoulders above the diminutive figure of Sir MacHinery. Cocking her head to one side she examined him carefully, mumbling to herself. The cat prowled cautiously around the robot's feet in a wide circle, sniffing curiously.

"Och, now," said the old woman at last, "couldn't ye have found a bigger one, Angus? No offence to ye, Sir Knight, but I fear ye be much too small for the work we have need of. Why the monster will gobble ye up for sure if—"

Angus hastily broke in. "Fwoosh, Maggie, we've

looked up and doon the land for nearly twelve months and nary a knight have we seen till now. Sir MacHinery is all we have and we must make the most o' him."

The witch fingered her chin, thoughtfully. "Ye're right, Angus," she sighed. "Big or little, he is all we have. But I dinna like to see a man get eaten wi' no chance at all. Sir Knight, ye must be clever and strong to do what has to be done. Ye may be clever, but I fear ye're much too small to be verra strong."

"Try him oot, Maggie," urged one of Angus' companions. "See if he can budge yon boulder."

"Aye," said the witch, and pointed to a large boulder, twice the size of the robot, which stood near the cave entrance. "See if ye can push that boulder a bit out o' place."

The robot walked to the rock, bent his knees, and scrabbled with his metal fingertips until he had a secure hold of the boulder's underside. Simon Smith had decided that a robot should be capable of lifting and moving heavy objects, and had accordingly fitted his pilot model with hydraulic jack muscles in each arm. The boulder was tremendously heavy, but it was no match for the mechanical leverage which the robot was able to exert. After several moments the huge rock began to lean noticeably, and then it suddenly teetered and fell with a loud thump. There was a shout of awe from the three brownies and Maggie's face broke into a gap-toothed smile of delight.

"Ye may do it, ye may do it!" she crowed. "We'll give it a try. Now listen, Sir Knight, to what we ask o' ye. There is but one way we can hope to beat the magic o' the demons, and that is wi' the help o' the greatest good wizard of the world. Merlin was his name and he lived long centuries ago. He was a friend to great King Arthur, and what Arthur and his knights couldna do to conquer evil wi' their swords and strength, Merlin did wi' his wisdom and power. But he fell in love at last wi' an evil witch woman who learned his magic from him and then betrayed him. She put him into a magical sleep and transported him to an enchanted cavern beneath a deep lake, and then she called up a fearsome monster to guard him. He is there still, and he is the only person in all the world who can match the magic o' the demons. But to set him free a man must beat the monster that guards him in a test o' riddles and strength. Now I must tell ye that many times in the past centuries knights have challenged the monster but none have ever beaten him. Are ye willing to try?"

"I am."

"Och, ye're a true and brave knight! The lake is Loch Bree, which lies halfway across Scotland from here. Ye'd best use my broom. Fetch it, Bathsheba."

The cat disappeared into the cave in a single bound and emerged an instant later with a broom in her mouth. It was an odd looking broom, made of a bundle of dried twigs tied to a gnarled tree branch handle. Taking it from the cat, Maggie handed it to the robot.

"Sit astride o' it, Sir MacHinery," she told him. "All ye need do is tell it where ye wish to go and it'll take ye there. You get on too, Angus."

The old brownie looked startled. "Must I, Maggie?" he asked in a tremulous voice. "I dinna hold wi' flyin' through the air."

"No foolishness now, Angus," said the old woman sharply. "Ye must go." Leaning close to him she whispered, "If he doesna beat the monster, ye must come back and tell me, so that we may plan something else."

Shaking his head, the old brownie straddled the broom handle behind the robot and clutched his metal sides. Then he closed his eyes.

"Tell it to take ye to Loch Bree," instructed Maggie. "Take us to Loch Bree," intoned the robot and, accompanied by a sickly moan from Angus, the broom immediately began to float skyward. Several hundred feet above Maggie's cave it circled uncertainly for a moment, and then with a surge of speed that made the air fairly whistle past it, it sped southward across the highlands to Loch Bree.

Chapter 4

The lake seemed as black as the bottom of a barrel of tar. Not a ripple disturbed its broad surface, which reflected the night sky like a huge mirror. From the mass of reeds and cattails, which surrounded its edge, came a constant croaking of frogs, and the whir and chirrup of a myriad of insects.

"Are ye ready?" Angus asked, a bit doubtfully.

"I am ready."

"Well," sighed the brownie, "let's have at it then. Gude luck to ye, Sir MacHinery."

Going down to the very edge of the water, he cupped his hands to his mouth and called out a string of Gaelic words which were meaningless to the robot. For a very long time nothing at all happened. Then, from far out in the middle of the lake, came a faint plopping sound. The calmness of the water was suddenly shattered by a series of wide ripples which came surging in toward the shore. And out in the inky blackness a deeper black something came sliding through the water, growing bigger as it came, until at last, with a rush and a swish and a snort and a splash, it flung itself up onto the beach, a huge, green black shape against the sky.

With his sensitive vision Sir MacHinery could see the monster quite clearly. It was a good thing that he was a machine and unable to feel fear, for the Loch Bree monster was a living remnant of an ancient time when both land and sea had been filled with massive, awe-inspiring reptiles. It was a dinosaur! A plesiosaur, to be exact, with a barrellike body, and long, snakelike neck atop which was a serpentine head filled with sharp teeth. The stars gleamed faintly on its sinuous, thirty-foot long, green body as it slithered across the sand toward Sir MacHinery.

Swinging its huge head down to ground level, it regarded the robot with obvious interest. "Ah, another knight!" it exclaimed in a husky whisper. "I suppose you've come to free Merlin, like all the others?"

"I have."

"Fine, fine." The monster seemed pleased. "It's been quite a while since I had any canned food. But tell me now—I don't wish to be rude, but aren't you rather small? Are you by any chance a boy? Surely, you aren't full grown?"

"I am not a boy," replied Sir MacHinery. "I am at my maximum level of height."

The monster wagged its head. "I certainly must admire your pluck," it said. "The last chap who came here was a great, big fellow who had quite a reputation as a giant killer, but he failed the test of strength quite badly. I hardly see how you can expect to stand up to it. Sure you want to go through with this?"

"I am sure."

The monster seemed to hunch its huge shoulders up

around its neck in a reptilian shrug. "Very well," it sighed. "Do you know the rules? First riddles, then we match strength, and if you lose either, I eat you. I go first. Now let me see—"

His voice trailed off and his yellow eyes closed in concentration. Sir MacHinery stood, completely motionless, waiting.

"Ah, here's a good one," exclaimed the monster, snapping open his eyes. "What animal is able to jump higher than the tallest mountain?"

Sir MacHinery's computor whirred into action, rapidly changing the words into mathematical expressions, and changing the whole into a mathematical formula. The robot could not be fooled by meanings of words; it operated by means of logic. A split second after the monster finished speaking, the robot had solved the equation and produced the simple, logical answer.

"Any animal can jump higher than a mountain," he intoned. "A mountain cannot jump."

"That was a pretty easy one, I guess," the monster grumbled. "But anyway, you're only halfway through. Now you have to stump me. Come on, ask me a riddle."

To Sir MacHinery the word *riddle* meant problem, and he had hundreds of problems stored away in his memory bank. With his camera-lens eyes staring levelly at the serpent head swaying before him, he asked a question, the answer to which is known to millions of schoolchildren: "What is the value of pi?"

The monster's head stopped swaying. "Pie?" it asked in a rather faint voice.

"Pi."

"Well, what sort of pie?" the monster asked, petulantly. "I mean there are mutton pies and mince pies and—"

"There is only one pi," interrupted the robot. "It is the expression of the ratio of the diameter of a circle to its circumference. What is the value of pi, expressed decimally?"

The monster was hopelessly befuddled. It had lived for millions of years and learned thousands of riddles, but it had a medieval mind to which even the most simple of twentieth-century mathematical problems was a mystery. It dropped its head onto the sand. After a while it rolled its eyes up toward the sky and snuffled. Then it rolled over onto its back and waved its flippers. At last, after nearly fifteen minutes had passed, it rolled over again, brought its head level with the robot and asked, "Is the answer five shillings?"

"No," said the robot. "The answer is three point one four one six."

"I'll take your word for it," sighed the monster, "although it really doesn't make any sense to me. But it's no matter—you're much too small to beat me in the test of strength, and unless you do, you'll lose the contest and I get to keep Merlin and eat you. Now then—"

It seemed to bunch itself together, coiling its sinuous neck like a huge spring. Then suddenly it shot forward, scuttling across the beach on its big flippers with surprising speed. It headed straight for a clump of trees clustered on the edge of the woods away from the beach. With a loud crack, which reverberated over the silent surface of the lake, it smashed into the nearest tree and snapped the trunk off, leaving a jagged and splintered stump. Then, it came swaggering back to the robot. "Now," it purred, "let's see you do that to one of the other trees."

With evenly spaced strides, the little robot marched across the sand until he reached the trees. He placed his metal palm flat against the bole of the largest one in the cluster. With an almost inaudible whine, tiny dynamos fed power into the hydraulic jack which was the muscle of his arm. And suddenly, with a report as loud as a gunshot, the tree broke cleanly in half.

"Hurrawhurroo!" Old Angus let out a screech of triumph. "Ye've done it, ye've done it, Sir MacHinery. Ye've won!"

The Loch Bree monster seemed frozen in surprise, staring in disbelief at the small silver figure which still stood with extended arm beside the sheared off tree trunk. Then, without a word, it turned and waddled sullenly to the water's edge. There it paused and twisted its neck to look back at the robot and the brownie who had gone to stand beside him. It curled its lip in scorn. With a loud splash it slid into the water and dove out of sight.

Angus trotted quickly down to the water's edge, and Sir MacHinery clumped across the pebbled beach behind him. Side by side they stared out across the black water. On the horizon, a faint flush of pink heralded the sunrise. Slowly a shape drifted toward them, resolving itself at last into a small boat in which stood the figure of a tall, robed man.

Chapter 5

The dawning sun had driven the inky blackness from the lake's surface and pushed the shadows away from the shore when the boat came to rest on the beach and its occupant stepped out. He was a tall, broadly built man, and although the hair that hung to his shoulders and the beard that spread across his chest was silver gray, there was a twinkle in his blue eyes and a quirk to his mouth that made him seem quite youthful. A rich, red brocaded robe, trimmed at the collar and cuffs with glossy brown fur, reached to his feet. He stood for a moment, glancing around the beach and up at the sky. Then he took a deep breath and his body shivered as though it contained a joy too great to hold.

"Free again at last!" he exclaimed. His deep, vibrant voice was touched with an odd but understandable accent. "There were times when I feared that I'd never again see the blessed sky nor feel a wind on my face." He bowed courteously and sincerely to the robot and brownie standing before him. "I am greatly in your debt. Whatever I may do to repay you—" his voice stopped in mid-sentence as he looked full upon Sir MacHinery for the first time. The little robot's gleaming figure was clearly visible in the ever-lightening dawn, and the man's eyebrows rose in astonishment.

"By the Red Dragon," he exclaimed, peering curiously at the small figure, "they've come a long way indeed since my day to be able to create something like this! What a wonder!"

"Och, indeed he is, great Merlin," Old Angus proudly stated. " 'Twas he who bested the monster and set ye free. He beat the beastie in the riddle contest and then, small though he be, he won the test o' strength. Why, I tell ye, Sir MacHinery is as gude a knight as ye ever saw even in the court of King Arthur!"

"Sir MacHinery?" said the wizard, incredulously. *"MacHinery?"* Suddenly, he slapped his thigh and burst into laughter.

"Aye," said Angus a trifle uncertainly. He wasn't sure why the wizard was laughing. "But great Merlin, we have no time for this. We braved the danger to set ye free because the world has great need o' ye once again. 'Tis the demon folk, Merlin. They are gettin' ready to come out again!"

"The demons," said the wizard musingly. "I never chanced to encounter them, but I know of the great war that was fought against them ages ago, and I know of their hatred for mankind and the upper world. If they break forth, it means they have somehow regained their ancient magic, or else made league with someone or *something* which provides them the power they need. At any rate, it bodes ill for the world, and it is well that you called me forth."

Striding to the lake's edge he bent down and scooped

up a handful of water which he let trickle through his fingers onto the sand. For a time he stood, staring down at the silver pool as though he saw more than just a puddle of water. After a while, he turned back to the brownie.

"After all my centuries of captivity, it still is not a bad world, Angus," he said, "but not really a good one, either. They've made themselves much more comfortable than the folk of my time, but they're not really much happier. They're just as greedy and quarrelsome as ever, and they've learned many more ways of hurting each other. But still, they're our kinfolk and it's our world too. We must help them, even though they'll never know it—unless we fail!"

Angus frowned. "Why canna we tell them, so they can help too?" he asked. "They have great armies and terrible weapons that can be used against the demons!"

The wizard grinned and shook his head. "This is an age of *logic,* brownie," he replied. "The people who could help us, the great lords and leaders, are the very ones who'd scoff at tales of demons and wizards and brownies. They believe only what they see with their eyes, and weigh in their scales, and prove with their equations. If we went among them they'd clap me into a madhouse and study you as a freak—but they'd not listen. Come now, let's see what the demons are doing. It's best to know what we're up against."

Bending to the water he again formed a small pool on the sand and knelt above it. Angus peered over his shoulder and watched in astonishment as the water flickered, turned silver and became a window, an opening through which they gazed upon a strange and terrifying sight.

It was apparently a huge cavern, deep inside the

earth. On each side, the cavern walls rose hundreds of feet until they were lost in the stygian blackness overhead. Blood red were these walls of rock, and completely covered with carvings chiseled into the hard stone by demon artists. Angus shuddered at what the carvings depicted; giant sculptures of men, women, children, elves, dwarves, brownies, and even animals of the forests, all fettered with heavy chains and bowed down in attitudes of grief, terror, and pain. Every creature who lived upon the earth's surface was shown, lining both sides of the cavern so that passing demons could see the creatures they hated, bowing in submission. Jutting forth at intervals between the carvings, were massive, ornamental pipes, which apparently tapped the gasses of the earth, for blue fire burned steadily at their tips.

The floor of the cavern was jet black, smooth, and shiny, and it thronged with hurrying demons. They swarmed along the broad road, popping in and out of circular holes that lined the walls on either side, driving chariots of gold and silver drawn by teams of giant, yellow-eyed rats. The demons were puffy and bulbous, their skins pallid gray and covered with lank, yellowish hair. Their heads were misshapen and overlarge, and their arms and legs were long, thin, and spidery, ending in red-clawed hands and feet. They dressed in tunics of rat skin, dyed deep shades of red, blue, and green, adorned with sparkling, many-faceted jewels. Their eyes were large, round, and staring, and their mouths were cruel gashes. Watching them, Angus again shuddered.

As the wizard and brownie continued their observation, something happened. The demons stopped their movement and all heads turned in one direction. They began to move in against the walls, leaving a wide path on the black highway. Through this opening in the vast crowd marched a column of demon soldiers, clad in black, scaled armor, and bearing silver axes. Behind them, drawn by four great black rats came a large, silver-wheeled, ebony chariot. In the chariot was a *thing!*

With all his squinting and peering, Angus could not quite make it out. It was like a black column of smoke which flowed and curled and altered, yet never changed in size or thickness. Deep within its uppermost portion glowed two red sparks, like eyes.

From Merlin came the sound of a sharply, indrawn breath. "Urlug!" he exclaimed.

Suddenly the black rats stopped, and the demon soldiers hurriedly formed a ring around the ebony chariot. The black shape seemed to twist this way and that, making Angus think of a hunting dog seeking a scent. Then, the thing coiled around, and the two red sparks were turned full in the direction of the peering man and brownie.

With another exclamation, Merlin swept his hand across the puddle, shattering the scene and leaving only a patch of wet sand. He sprang to his feet. "We must get away from here. Quickly!" he said sharply.

Seizing the robot, he tucked its child-sized body under one arm, scooped up the astonished and somewhat indignant brownie with the other, and dashed up the sandy slope with speed that would have done credit to a ten-year-old. After covering some five hundred yards he stopped, panting for breath. "Angus," he said, "we must find shelter somewhere."

"We still have plenty o' time," said the brownie a

bit crossly, clambering down the wizard's robe to the ground. "The morning's wee yet. Menfolk'll not be aboot for hours."

Merlin shook his head impatiently. "It's not men I care about," he snapped. "Urlug saw us spying on him and —" abruptly he stopped and stared out toward the lake. "Too late," he said, softly. "Look there."

The brownie glanced toward the lake. A small patch of fog was creeping in off the water. As he watched, it billowed up to the very spot where he and the wizard had knelt only moments before while peering through the window. Oddly, it seemed to pause at this spot, twisting and curling. Suddenly, Angus remembered how the black thing in the chariot had twisted and curled like a creature seeking a scent, before its red eyes had turned in their direction. For the third time that morning he shuddered. Turning to the wizard he asked, "Be that real fog or somethin' else?"

"It is a sending from the thing we saw in the demon's cavern," Merlin answered. "Sent to find us. The thing was Urlug, a creature of great power from the blackest, evil pits in the depths of the earth. The demons seem to have made a most powerful alliance. It has powers I cannot match. That patch of fog can neither see nor hear, but unless we can get away from here quickly it will find us and we will be in Urlug's power!"

As they watched, the patch of gray began to billow slowly over the ground following the exact path that Merlin had taken in his dash for shelter. "It's hunting us doon," moaned Angus.

"Yes," said the wizard. "It moves slowly, but it can follow us as long as we move along the ground. I have a spell for flying through the air, but without certain magic tools I cannot perform it."

Suddenly, in his precise, mechanical voice, Sir MacHinery spoke. "We can fly through the air with the witch's broom."

"Of course," Merlin exclaimed. They could see the broom lying on the sand some twenty yards from the gray creeping mass. "MacHinery," said the magician, "run as fast as you can and bring the broom to us. *Do not let that gray shape touch you!*" He realized that the robot was probably capable of extreme speed.

He was right. With a thin whine Sir MacHinery's hydraulic leg muscles turned his legs into silver blurs as he sped to the broom, deftly snatching it up, and rushed back to the others.

The foglike patch crept nearer. Merlin straddled the broom. "MacHinery, sit in front of me," he instructed, "and hold Angus on your lap." The brownie moaned with anguish at the prospect of flying again, but scrambled onto the robot's lap. Sir MacHinery's arms closed gently and firmly around him.

In a clear, loud voice Merlin said, "Take us back to the cave of Maggie MacMurdoch."

As before, the broom slowly rose, circled about for a moment, then began to rush through the air some two-hundred feet off the ground. Glancing back, Merlin saw the gray, foggy mass hovering uncertainly over the spot they had just left. Abruptly, it vanished.

Chapter 6

The witch's broom traveled with amazing swiftness, and it was still quite early when it passed over the castle atop Auld Clootie, slowed down, and spiraled to a stop a few feet above the ground in front of the cave home of Maggie MacMurdoch. At that moment, she and her cat appeared in the cave entrance. The old woman took a few steps forward, her eyes peering intently into those of the tall, bearded man. Then she inclined her head in a gesture of respect. The magician bowed gravely in return.

"I didna think he could really do it," said the good witch softly, turning her gaze upon the small figure of Sir MacHinery. "He must be one of the greatest of all knights."

Merlin's face broke into a grin. "He's much more than that, Maggie MacMurdoch," he said. "But if we may enter your home, I'll tell you all about him." His grin vanished. "I'll also tell you what I've learned of the demons. They are in league with a dark, evil power, and it is searching us out. You must help me lay spells of protection, while we decide what to do."

"Och!" hissed the woman. " 'Tis worse than I feared. By all means, enter my home, great Merlin." She hobbled back into the cave, the cat at her side, and they followed her.

The inside of the cave was not like a cave at all, but like a home with wood-panelled rooms, and neat flagstone floors. The witch led them through a short hall and into a room filled with an assortment of strange objects. A bright fire burned in a fireplace.

A pile of huge, leather-bound books filled one corner and reached almost to a shelf on the wall upon which stood a row of bottles, containing such ingredients as powdered bat wings and toe of newt. Next to the books stood an enormous green bottle, inside of which was a slightly smaller red bottle, with a still smaller blue bottle inside of it. On one wall hung a murky mirror, which did not seem to reflect anything, and on the opposite wall hung a painting of a man's face with a real beard growing out of it. The center of the room was occupied by a massive wooden table upon which were a crystal ball, a stuffed raven with a red ribbon tied around its beak, and a small box with a door painted on it. On the painted door was a sign which said DANGER—KEEP OUT!

"This is where I cast my spells, great Merlin," said Maggie, somewhat apologetically. "I know it canna compare wi' what you're used to, but I think I have everything ye need."

"You're very well equipped," replied the wizard gallantly, glancing about. He winked at the bearded painting, which winked back, picked up a heavy mortar and pestle, and began selecting items from the witch's shelves.

After he and Maggie had been busily at work for

nearly an hour, Merlin said, "That should do it. I think we can talk now without being spied upon. Is anything watching us?" he asked the bearded painting.

"No," said the painting in a gruff voice. "All is well."

"Very good," said the wizard, seating himself on a corner of the table, while the witch settled herself in a chair. "Now I can tell you what we face."

"Urlug is a creature of pure evil and great power. He is not as strong as the power that originally created the demons ages ago, but his power is stronger than yours and mine together, Maggie."

"What can we do?" asked the woman softly.

"Urlug can be destroyed," declared Merlin, "but only by a weapon of great power in the hands of a true hero. I know of such a weapon if it has not been removed in the years during my imprisonment."

Slipping from the table, he stood before the murky mirror. "Still there!" He exulted, peering into the mirror's depths.

"What is it, Merlin?" squeaked Angus from his corner.

"It is the sword of Sir Galahad," answered Merlin. "When Galahad was searching for the Holy Grail, he came upon the sword that had been forged with great magic more than a thousand years before, by King Solomon. It is a weapon of great power over evil, but it can only be wielded by one who has no fear, who has more than mortal strength, and who cannot be tricked or tempted away from his purpose. Galahad was such a man, and so were Arthur and Seigfried and Roland. But where are we to find such a champion now?"

Again he seated himself on the table. The brownie came to stand beside him. "I see what ye mean Merlin," he acknowledged. " 'Twill be verra hard to find such a one. A man who has great strength may yet be a coward. A man who knows no fear may not have the wit to keep from bein' tricked or tempted."

"Yes," said the wizard grimly. "Where indeed do we find one?"

Sinking his chin on his chest, he frowned in concentration, gazing absently at the figure of the little robot standing silently against one wall. "It must be someone most extraordinary; someone who—"

His voice broke off suddenly and his eyes, still gazing at the robot, widened. "Why, of course!" he exclaimed, and laughed with surprise and pleasure. "We have the perfect champion right with us!"

"I never understand what's goin' on," Angus complained. "Who d'ye mean, Merlin?"

The wizard pointed. "Your 'Sir MacHinery,' " he answered. "*He* is our champion. You see, Angus and Maggie, Sir MacHinery is not a mortal man in armor as you've been thinking. He is a *machine*—a machine that can think and talk and move. But, a machine cannot be afraid and cannot be turned aside from its purpose. *He* can use the sword!"

Angus was astounded by this revelation that what he had thought to be a small man in a suit of armor was a machine. He stared in wonder at the silver robot, as did Maggie MacMurdoch.

"Och," said the witch, " 'tis a wonder! I had heard there was a mad scientist in Strathgow castle. It must be he who made this mechanical man. These modern scientists put us witches and wizards to shame wi' what they can do, Merlin."

"They have certainly given us what we could never

have found in any other way," replied the magician. "This mechanical man will probably be the greatest champion ever called upon to fight against evil. He can never tire, never feel fear; his strength is incredible, and he will do exactly what must be done. Above all else, he is intelligent. He bested the Loch Bree monster in the contest of riddles, and it was he who thought of the way to escape from Urlug's magic that sought us out." He smiled at the robot.

"You may be just a machine, Sir MacHinery, but you are a person, nonetheless."

"Well," observed Angus contentedly, folding his arms, "we have the champion, and ye know where the weapon is, so let's get on wi' it and give this Urlug and the demons a thrashin'!"

The wizard's smile faded. "There are still a few obstacles, brownie," he sighed. "To begin with, Galahad's sword is buried at Stonehenge in England."

"Well," said Angus again, "that's not an obstacle. Let's take a shovel there and dig it up."

Merlin shook his head. "You don't know about Stonehenge, I see. It is a ring of huge stones put up thousands of years ago by a savage and primitive people. It is a curiosity that is visited daily by hundreds of persons, so we certainly could not dig up the sword in the middle of a throng of tourists, as I believe they are called."

"Do it at night then!" exclaimed the brownie.

The wizard smoothed his beard. "After Galahad died his sword was seized by certain evil magicians," he said. "They buried it at Stonehenge and put it under guard. It is guarded by the dark spirits of the people who built Stonehenge, which was a bloody and horrible place of sacrifice for them. Were we to enter Stonehenge at night and attempt to gain the sword, these black ghosts would rise against us. And they have a certain power; a spell of terror that will render any mortal man helpless. Not even I can combat this power."

"What of Sir MacHinery?" interjected Maggie. "He would not fear these ghosties. Could he go in and dig up the sword?"

"The sword was buried by magic and can only be raised by magic," Merlin replied. "No; somehow the dark spirits must be driven off so that I can enter Stonehenge and raise the sword."

At that moment there was a sudden and disturbing interruption. The bearded painting spoke with urgency. "Someone is attempting to break through the barrier and enter this house," it announced.

Chapter 7

When he awoke from his much needed night's sleep with a yawn and stretch, Simon Smith's first thought was his robot. He could hardly wait to begin the tests. Hurriedly throwing on a pair of jeans, an old sweat shirt, and a pair of battered loafers, he rinsed his face from a basin of cold water which stood beside the bed on an ornately carved nightstand. He had not bothered to shave for several weeks and had a tangled growth of beard.

Not even stopping for a cup of coffee, he hurried downstairs to the main hall where he had left the robot. Thrusting open the great door, he rushed into the room, only to stop short in consternation at the sight of the empty chair.

His first thought was that the robot had somehow toppled over, so he got down on all fours and peered beneath the legs of the chair and table. Then he stood up and stared desperately about the great hall. His eye lit on a mouse hole and, seaching for some explanation, he decided that perhaps a mouse had emerged from the hole, climbed upon the robot, and somehow accidentally pressed the activating button. Leaping for the door he impatiently tugged it open and began a frantic search of the entire castle. After thoroughly combing the castle for better than an hour and finding nothing, he came to the conclusion that the robot had been stolen. Since the only people nearby, so far as he knew, were the citizens of Strathgow, it seemed obvious that one or more of them had sneaked into the castle during the night and made off with his precious model robot. Rushing from the castle, he hurled himself into his car and roared down the cart road to the town.

Reaching Strathgow, which was just beginning to stir with morning activity, he drove wildly through the streets until he saw the figure of Constable Wier, strolling about on his morning rounds. The constable was dressed in full uniform of dome-shaped helmet and brass-buttoned, dark blue coat. However, he had always refused to wear the blue, regulation police trousers, preferring to wear a kilt instead, so the overall effect of his appearance was something unusual. Simon brought his car to a screeching stop in the middle of the street and pelted toward him. "My robot!" he shouted. "My robot's been stolen!"

If Constable Wier's appearance was unusual to the physicist, Simon's appearance was even more unusual to the policeman. The constable had not seen the American since the first day he had driven into town, at which time he had been clean shaven. Now, the sight of the disreputably clothed, bearded figure charging down upon him startled the constable considerably. For a moment he was about to call for help, but then he recognized the American's car and realized who the man was. He knew that

Smith was a scientist, and, like many ordinary folk, had a sort of feeling that scientists, artists, writers, and actors all had a kind of freedom to look as unusual as they pleased. He instinctively forgave Smith for his appearance, for which he would have chided one of Strathgow's citizens. "What's that ye're sayin' Professor Smith, sir," he asked politely. "I didn'a quite ken it."

"My robot!" Simon repeated almost tearfully. "My robot has been stolen!"

Constable Wier hadn't the faintest notion what a robot was, but he knew that scientists frequently used animals in their experiments, so he leaped to the conclusion that Smith was talking about something like a hamster or guinea pig. "Now, now," he said gently, "perhaps ye merely forgot to lock its cage and it's simply wandered oot."

Simon stared at him. "Cage," he said stupidly. "Why should I keep it in a cage?"

Constable Wier shook his head. "Och, now," he said seriously, "no matter how tame it may have been ye canna expect it to stay put if ye dinna keep it caged. Like as not it slipped oot o' the castle and is rootin' aboot in the woods."

Simon shook his head. "Impossible," he said. "I hadn't brought it to life yet."

The police officer favored him with a long stare, during which his eyes slowly widened. The mystery of the mad American scientist was at last cleared up. "Ye mean," he said in a shocked whisper, "that ye're experimentin' at bringin' *dead* things to life?"

A number of the folk of Strathgow appeared while

this conversation was taking place and eased in closer to hear as much as they could. Most of them were near enough to hear Constable Wier's whisper, and there was a general gasp of horror. Old Ritchie MacMullin let out a triumphant wheeze. "I told ye, I told ye!" he croaked. "He's a mad scientist makin' monsters from parts o' dead things! A Frankenstein he is!"

Simon stared about at the ring of horrified faces. "Don't any of you know what a robot is?" he demanded. "It's not a dead thing; it's a machine! I've built a machine that can think and move and work like a human being And one of you has stolen it!"

"Now, now," said Constable Wier, sharply, "that's a serious charge Professor! Why would anyone here take yer machine? What could they do wi' it?"

"Why, they could—" began Smith, then stopped short. Looking at the faces of these simple people he realized that if none of them even knew what a robot was, they could hardly realize its value. "I don't know," he answered miserably, and attempted an explanation. "Look here, folks, a robot is a mechanical man. It's designed to do work like digging coal or working in a steel mill and things like that. I designed it and built it with the idea that such machines could help free men from most of the hard and dangerous jobs they have to do now. I spent every cent I had on the parts for it and was going to activate it, that is, start it up, this morning. But when I woke up, it was gone from the castle."

A great light had dawned in the eyes of most of the crowd that surrounded the physicist. This, they could understand, and they approved of it. Simon Smith was not a mad scientist making monsters, but a fine man working to make life easier for people. Several of them removed their caps in reverence.

"Well now, I think I do understand," said Constable Wier grimly. "It does sound as if someone has made off wi' yer mechanical man, Professor, but I think I can tell ye for sure it was no one from here in Strathgow."

"Well, who then?" asked Simon glumly, thrusting his hands into the pockets of his tattered jeans.

There was a long silence, then Ritchie MacMullin cleared his throat. "It could only have been the Wee Folk!"

"The *who?*" asked Simon, vaguely.

"The Wee Folk," said Constable Wier, nodding. "The Little People. Some call 'em pixies."

"Pixies?" said Simon in amazement. "You mean like little elves and fairies and things that dance around under toadstools?" He made wiggling dance motions with his fingers.

"The Wee Folk are just the Wee Folk!" declared Mr. Darling, positively. "And if they've taken yer mechanical man, there's naught ye can do aboot it!"

"Perhaps," said old Ritchie slowly, "Maggie MacMurdoch would know."

"Who's Maggie MacMurdoch?" queried Simon.

"Och, she's the witch that lives up on the mountain not far from yer castle," replied the old man.

Simon Smith exploded. "Do you actually mean to tell me," he said loudly, turning in a slow circle, "that you people still believe in witches and pixies and that sort of thing in this day and age. I mean, really believe?"

"Well o' course," said Mr. Darling in an injured tone

of voice. "You've made a live mechanical man have ye not? It's all the same sort o' thing."

"It is not!" yelled Simon, momentarily forgetting his loss. "You're talking about superstition and metaphysical nonsense. What I did was a simple application of physical laws and electronic principles. Oh, well," he sighed. "Why argue. Tell me where this Maggie Macwhat's-her-name lives, and I'll see if she knows anything. I've got to find my robot."

The retired army man, Sergeant Major Small, spoke up. "Ye'd get lost in the woods up there, laddie," he said. "I'll go wi' ye and show ye the way."

"This is police business," said Constable Wier, officiously. "So I shall go wi' ye too and conduct the investigation." Never having had an investigation to conduct, he was enthralled at the prospect.

The two men climbed into the car, and Simon Smith drove back up to the castle atop Auld Clootie. "We'll have to go on foot from here," remarked Sergeant Major Small. Following a barely visible path, they made their way to the foot of the mountain.

They had been in the woods only a short time when, to his everlasting credit, (and surprise) Constable Wier found a clue. "Look here," he cried in excitement. There was a slightly muddy patch near the path, and clearly imprinted in it was the mark of a small, oddly shaped foot.

"That's my robot's footprint," exclaimed Simon. "Good for you, Officer Wier; we're on the right track."

Constable Wier swelled with visible pride. "All in the line o' duty, sir," he said stiffly, touching his fingers to the bill of his helmet in a polite salute.

The three men were wheezing a bit when they finally

emerged from the forest into the clearing outside Maggie MacMurdoch's cave. "You mean she lives in there?" said Simon distastefully. "Boy, what a kook she must be!"

He strode toward the opening, entered the shadows, and came to an abrupt halt. "Hey, this is no cave," he called. "There's just a plain, blank, rock wall!"

"What?" exclaimed Sergeant Small and Constable Wier in unison. Hurrying forward, Small reached out a hand and timorously felt the solid rock. "I dinna understand," he mused. "I have been here many times, years ago, and there was a door here."

"Are you sure it's the right cave?" asked Simon Smith. "Maybe it's somewhere farther along the mountainside."

"Nay, this be it," declared Constable Wier. "I've been here mysel' a time or two and there was a door! I dinna ken this at all!"

Then, as the three men stood silently, each wondering what to do, the wall of rock suddenly shimmered and became a wooden door which swung slowly open.

Chapter 8

Inside the witch's magic room, a moment of silence followed the bearded picture's announcement. Then Merlin said softly, "Can you judge their intentions?"

"Not evil," stated the painting. "I do not believe they come from Urlug. There are three of them, all mortals. Two appear to be rather frightened, and the other is angry and concerned."

Merlin grunted. "Perhaps it's safe to look at them." He stepped to the murky mirror and peered into it. "They do seem to be just ordinary mortals, but we cannot be too careful. Maggie, do you know them?"

The witch hobbled to the mirror. " 'Tis Constable Wier and Sergeant Small o' Strathgow," she said. "But I dinna know the one wi' the beard."

"Let me see," pleaded Angus. Merlin lifted the brownie up so that he could peer into the mirror. "I know him," said Angus. " 'Tis the foreigner who's been livin' in the castle where we found Sir MacHinery."

"Well, well, well!" exclaimed the wizard. "So that is the man who constructed MacHinery. I would like to meet him. A man as wise and skillful as he could be of great help to us. Maggie, may I ask you to invite these men into your home and bring them here?"

"Of course, Great Merlin," answered the witch, and made her way down the passage toward the door, which swung open as she reached it. She nodded to the three men who stood, open-mouthed, in the doorway. "Will ye please to enter, gentlemen," she said, and added, "quickly."

Simon strode in at once, followed hesitantly by the two Scotsmen. The door thumped shut behind them, which made Wier and Small jump apprehensively, but the physicist scarcely noticed. "Are you Maggie?" he demanded. "Do you know anything about my robot? It's a machine that looks like—"

Maggie interrupted with a smile. "Come this way please," she said gently. As Smith entered the magic room, the small silver figure of his robot caught his eye at once.

"There it is!" he yelled joyfully, rushing to the robot's side. Bending over, he examined his handiwork carefully. "Seems to be in order," he mumbled. "I hope they didn't jar anything loose when they dragged him here."

"I was not dragged," the robot informed him. "I walked."

Smith jerked upright in surprise. "You've activated him!" he exclaimed, glaring at the witch and the tall, robed and bearded man, who was watching with an amused expression. "You could have ruined everything by messing around with something you don't understand! Officer Wier, I want you to arrest these people for stealing my robot."

"One moment," said Merlin, calmly. "I understand

your concern, but let me put your mind at ease. The machine is not in the least harmed. I fully appreciate what a great work of art this mechanical marvel is, and what it means to you."

"Oh, you do, do you," replied Simon belligerantly. "Well, just who the heck are you, anyway?"

"My name," said the wizard with twinkling eyes, "is Merlin."

Simon stared at him, rubbed his nose thoughtfully, then glanced up at the ceiling. "Not by any chance," he said in a tone of exaggerated awe, "*the* Merlin of King Arthur's Court?"

"I'm afraid so," said the wizard, rubbing his mouth to cover a grin.

"Oh, boy! Pixies, witches, and now Merlin," sighed the physicist. He bowed low. "Well, allow me to introduce myself. I am Mother Goose!"

Merlin chuckled openly, and turned his head slightly. "Do you see now what I meant, Angus," he remarked, "when I told you this was an age of disbelief?"

The brownie, who had been hiding behind the table, came forward a few steps and revealed himself. Simon stared at his foot-tall figure, then stepped forward and tentatively prodded Angus at his belt line with one finger. The brownie angrily slapped it away.

"H'm," mused the physicist. "You could be a hypnotic illusion of course, but I rather suspect that you're simply an exceedingly small midget." He stood up and glanced around. "I think I'm beginning to get it," he announced. "You're putting together some sort of circus sideshow and you wanted my robot as one of your attractions."

Merlin chuckled again. "You see, Angus?" he said. "His disbelief will always allow him to find what he regards as a rational explanation."

"Aye," sighed the brownie. But then he pointed at the constable and Sergeant Small, who had been gazing about the room in awe, and were now staring at him in wide-eyed wonder. "But they believe, do they not?"

"Oh, yes," said the wizard. "However *this* is the sort of man we need." He nodded toward Smith. "And we must have his robot."

"You're not getting my robot for any sideshow," Smith said angrily, but the wizard held up his hand.

"Let me explain," he pleaded. Very quickly he told the story of the war that occurred untold ages before, of the new threat of the demons and their powerful ally, of his release from the lake by Sir MacHinery, and of their realization that only the robot could wield the Sword of Power, defeat the terrible creature from the netherworld, and thwart the demons. Simon listened to all this with facial expressions that changed from disbelief, to derision, to tolerant amusement. When Merlin had finished, the physicist shook his head.

"That's one of the wildest tales I ever heard," he grinned. "You may not be a real magician, old boy, but you've got a heck of a good imagination. You could sell that story to any science fiction magazine in the world."

Constable Wier spoke up. "Dinna be hasty, Professor Smith," he said grimly. "Ye dinna understand this part o' the world. I've seen many strange things in my time and heard o' stranger, and if the demons are on the move—I'm afeard!"

Simon made an impatient gesture. "Look, I'm willing to admit that there may be some primitive race living in these mountains, and that they plan to come out and make trouble, but why not simply notify the authorities? Why all this mumbo jumbo about shadowy beings from the depths of the earth, and magic swords and witchcraft? As I say, why not just notify the proper authorities in Glasgow or Edinburgh, and let them handle the problem."

"Firstly, because they would not believe me any more than you do," answered Merlin, "and secondly, because even if we could convince them, it would take far too long for any action to be taken." He shook his head. "We cannot wait. We must move now or it will be too late."

"Well that's just too bad," declared Simon Smith, "because I think you're a bunch of nuts. I won't prefer charges against you, but I'm taking my robot and getting out of here right now."

Merlin was not sure what he would have done had Simon attempted to carry out his threat. He momentarily considered putting the three mortals under a spell of sleep, but the problem was solved for him by an unexpected source.

"I will not go with you," Sir MacHinery announced in his monotone voice, turning his head in Simon Smith's direction.

"Huh?" was all that Smith could say.

"When you constructed me," intoned the robot, "you programmed me to protect human life at all cost. I am incapable of harming any human being. I am programmed to sacrifice myself, if necessary, to protect a human. If I do not destroy Urlug, which is a nonhuman creature, and the demons break forth, the human race will be harmed.

My programming will not permit me to let this occur."

Simon looked pleased. "Well, that's one test I won't have to make," he said, almost to himself. "Your programming regarding the sanctity of human life is certainly in order. But see here, robot. I tell you there is no danger to humanity from these demons. They may not even exist. And your own logic should tell you that there is no such thing as magic. It contradicts the laws of physics. This man Merlin's story is impossible."

"Your own logic is faulty," replied the robot. "You have formed a judgment without evidence. With my own sensors, I viewed the monster from which I freed Merlin. Within my memory bank is the evidence of two journeys through the air on what appeared to be an ordinary broom. If these portions of Merlin's story are true, you must admit the rest may well be true also."

The physicist stared at his creation and fingered his chin. "You say you flew on a *broom?*" he asked at last.

"Affirmative," stated the robot.

"Well, in the first place, that's aerodynamically impossible," commented the physicist. "But what's more important, there wouldn't be any propelling force. This can be proved mathematically." He glanced about. "Say, have you got a blackboard or some paper handy? If I could work out some equations I could show the impossibility of—"

Merlin gave one of his booming laughs, and striding across the room placed a hand on the physicist's shoulder. "I know exactly how you feel. Many is the time when I spent hours and even days on a problem which I was determined to either solve or disprove. We have much in common, you and I, whether you think so or not. And I ask you—is it not possible that what I call magic, and you call science, are simply two different ways of solving certain problems?"

Smith found himself suddenly liking this big, hearty man. He reminded him greatly of a professor who had been a favorite of his during his undergraduate days at college. Nevertheless he grumbled, "Not when your magic contradicts physical laws. Science isn't based on mumbo jumbo."

"Well, whatever you think of it," said Merlin gently, "will you not join us? I have the feeling that there may well be things which I cannot do with my mumbo jumbo, as you put it, that you may be able to do with your science."

Simon shrugged. "I don't seem to have much choice. My own robot refuses to come with me, and I'll be darned if I'll let him out of my sight again."

Sergeant Major Small cleared his throat and took a step forward. "Sir," he said, "may I join ye too? I'm not a young man I know, but I was a soldier, and a gude one, for twenty-five years. I could help, I know I could." His gray moustache bristled as he thrust his chin forward and drew himself to attention. "I can still fight!"

Merlin regarded him, thoughtfully. "You remind me of someone I knew long ago," he said, "only he was a younger man. His name was Lancelot. Of course you may join us."

Now the constable stepped forward. "As Her Majesty's representative in this area," he said, "I think I should come too. I'm sworn to uphold the peace and the law and if the Wee Folk are aboot to disrupt it, 'tis my duty to oppose them."

"Our wee army is growin'," observed Maggie.

Simon Smith shook his head in wonder. "I still think you're all a bunch of nuts." he commented.

Chapter 9

"Now then," said Merlin briskly, "we have much to do. First," he turned to the two Scotsmen, "your absence from the town of Strathgow will have to be explained somehow. Otherwise, search parties will be out looking for you and that could draw Urlug's attention to us here."

"I'll take care o' that," said the Sergeant Major. "I'll go back and tell the folks that the constable and I are stayin' at the castle wi' the professor. Anyway, there's a few things I want to get from my home." He snapped a salute, spun on his heel, and they heard his footsteps marching briskly down the hall.

"Is he safely past the barrier?" asked Merlin after a a moment.

"Yes," said the bearded painting. Simon jumped as did Constable Wier. Then the physicist hurried to the painting and stared at it. Experimentally, he tugged at its beard.

"Ouch!" said the painting. "Stop that or I'll bite your finger!"

Simon grinned at Merlin. "You're quite a ventriloquist too, I see," he remarked. Strolling back to the wizard, he looked him in the eye. "Now, what about this sword you say you must have? You say it's buried at Stonehenge under the protection of a bunch of evil ghosts? How do you plan to get it?"

"Aye, Merlin," piped up Angus. "Ye were aboot to tell me that when these mortals came to the door. "If we canna face these things because o' their power, how can we fight them? For that matter, how do ye fight a ghostie at all? Ye canna cut it wi' a sword. Ye canna bash it wi' a club."

"He has a point there," observed Simon with a grin. "As I understand it, a ghost is a nonmaterial being that can walk through walls and all that sort of nonsense. Therefore, theoretically, it can't be harmed by any material object. So how are you going to fight these nasty, evil spirits, wizard?"

Merlin's eyes twinkled. "With other ghosts," he replied calmly.

The physicist closed his eyes. "I'm sorry I asked," he murmured. Rubbing his nose, a gesture which for him indicated amused disbelief, he said, "No doubt you have a number of ghostly friends?"

"Several, as a matter of fact," smiled the wizard. "But they're not what I have in mind. My plan is to raise an army of ghosts—ghosts of men who, when they lived, were fierce and courageous fighters. Fortunately for us, the country of Scotland has been filled with such men throughout its history."

Angus grunted in assent. "Aye, that's the truth. Why, when they couldna find any ootsiders to fight wi', they'd even fight each other. I think I see what ye mean,

Merlin; an army o' stout-hearted ghosties will not be afeared o' other ghosties."

"This is an academic question," put in Simon, "but can these ghosts injure one another? I mean, if one ghost punches another in the nose, can he cause a ghostly nosebleed?"

Merlin shook his head. "They are as immaterial to one another as they are to us."

"Well then it'll be like fighting a duel with two flashlight beams," exclaimed Simon, rumpling his already tousled hair. "Theoretically they'll simply go right through each other! I don't see how—"

"I'm relying upon the power of courage to overcome terror," Merlin broke in. "I believe that if I can raise an army of the right sort, their very love of battle and desire to win will prevail and drive off the dark guardians of the sword."

Simon shrugged. "That's as logical as anything else about this illogical mess," he commented. "When will you raise this ghostly army? I suppose it has to be done after midnight, with all the proper spells and incantations?"

"As a matter of fact, you're quite right," grinned Merlin. "As soon as the sun sets, which should only be a few hours from now, I shall begin my preparations. You may help if you wish."

"Gladly," said Simon. "Do I sprinkle the powdered unicorn horn or stir the bubbly cauldron with the shinbone of a giant?"

Merlin chuckled and turned to Maggie. "May we prevail upon your hospitality for some food, Maggie MacMurdoch?" he asked. The witch inclined her head, hobbled from the room, and returned a short time later with a huge platter heaped with slices of home-baked bread, oatcakes, cheese, and cold duck. Setting this on the table, she hurried off again and was quickly back with four, large mugs of foaming ale, and a thimble into which a bit of the drink was poured for Angus. In her corner, Bathsheba slurped noisily at a saucer of thickly creamed milk.

They had finished their simple but excellent supper and settled back with satisfied sighs, when the bearded painting spoke again.

"The other mortal has returned," it announced.

"Let him in," said Maggie.

After a moment, into the room came an utterly transformed Sergeant Major Small. He was wearing his full dress uniform of World War II. On the right sleeve of his khaki-colored tunic were four chevrons, and a double row of battle ribbons blazed above his upper left pocket flap. His kilt was that of the 42nd Regiment of Highlanders, the Black Watch, most famed regiment in the Scottish Division of the British army. Under his arm was a British Sten gun—a type of light machine gun—and slung across his shoulder was a bulging canvas bag.

"Still fits," he chortled, patting the waist of his uniform. "I have not put on an ounce o' fat since '45."

"What's in that bag?" demanded Constable Wier, suspiciously.

"Seven ammunition clips for the Sten and three o' these," replied Small, reaching into the bag and pulling forth a hand grenade.

"What is that?" asked Merlin curiously.

"Something to give yer demons a bit o' a shock." replied the ex-soldier. "Ye see, ye simply pull this pin oot, count three, and throw it. When it comes doon it goes off wi' a bang and throws bits o' metal aboot like bullets. I knocked oot a German machine gun nest wi' one o' these in Africa. Blew 'em to kingdom come."

Merlin stroked his beard with an air of disapproval. "As I have noted, mankind's ability to wreak destruction upon himself has grown greatly since the days when I helped Arthur wage his wars. However, these objects may be of considerable use in combating the demons, I must admit."

"You're just in time Sergeant," Simon remarked jocularly. "The wizard here is about to raise an army."

Sergeant Small looked perplexed. "Well, I dinna quite see where ye'll get it from, sir," he observed, staring at Merlin.

With a sigh, the wizard quickly repeated the story of the buried Sword of Power and its evil guardians, and his plans to combat them with an army of the ghosts of Scottish warriors. By the time he finished, Small was nodding vigorously.

" 'Tis a gude plan, sir," he commented enthusiastically. "I can tell ye that if ye give a Scotsman the chance at a bonnie battle, he'll be the best fightin' man ye could want, whether he's alive or a ghostie."

"Apparently he believes you can do it, too," Simon snorted. "Well it seems to be getting dark outside, and I am most anxious to observe how you go about materializing these nonmaterial ghosties who are going to fight a nonmaterial battle against a nonmaterial foe."

"Come and observe then," replied Merlin, rising to his feet. Silently, they all followed him outside into the clearing before the cave. The forest around them was already full of dark, looming shadows, and the sun was no more than a deep red ball, fast dropping out of sight.

By midnight a great roaring fire had been built by the magician with the help of Simon, the constable, Sergeant Small, Angus, and the other two brownies whom Simon had regarded with some surprise. Many branches had been cut and piled to form the shape of a five-pointed star; certain powders and herbs had been sprinkled atop them, and Merlin, with the help of Maggie, began the spell. Moving together, they began to walk around the fire in an intricate pattern that seemed almost like a dance, chanting softly in unison as they did so. To the three men and the brownies, watching from the forest edge, they appeared as black silhouettes when they passed in front of the fire and as eerie, red lit shapes when they reached the other side. The brownies, seated cross-legged, observed the procedure with calm, matter-of-factness. Constable Wier and Sergeant Small stared in unblinking nervousness, and Simon Smith frequently rubbed his nose and grinned.

Abruptly, the chanting stopped, and the two figures became motionless. The blaze died down and the smoke began to thicken and billow, becoming suffused with a rainbow of ever changing colors which writhed and swirled and soared up out of sight into the night sky. Merlin suddenly flung up both arms.

"William Wallace, awaken and come forth!" he called in a loud, commanding voice.

The smoke swirled as though blown by a sudden gust of wind, and abruptly a pale figure stepped forward from it into the clearing. It was a tall man dressed in chain mail, with a conical helmet upon his head and a great broadsword strapped to his side. Every detail of his body could be seen, yet the firelight and the smoke showed clearly through it.

From the forest's edge there were three gasps, followed by a heavy thud.

"Ye'd best fan yer professor friend wi' yer hat," suggested Angus to Constable Wier. "I think he's fainted."

Chapter 10

The ghost of William Wallace stood with folded arms beside the guttering fire. His bearded face was grim and lined, and his eyes piercing. During his lifetime, six-hundred years before, he had devoted his life to keeping his country free, only to be captured and horribly tortured by his enemies. But his memory had united the Scottish people in their desire for freedom.

"Robert the Bruce, awaken and come forth!" called Merlin again.

A second pale and transparent figure stepped from the eddying smoke. He was clad much like Wallace, but in his mailed fist was a great battle-ax. This was Wallace's successor who, as King of the Scots, had fought and won the great battle of Bannockburn and driven the enemy from Scotland's soil.

One after another, Merlin called out the names of Scotland's most famous fighting men and, one after another, ghostly figures stepped forth from the writhing smoke. There was Black Douglas, Bonnie Dundee, Rob

Roy MacGregor, Red Douglas, MacGillivray of Dunmaglass, Ranald of Clanranald, and scores of other chieftains and officers who had fearlessly led men of Highlands and Lowlands in battles all over the world. There were hundreds of men of lesser fame and lower rank as well, who had fought in all the battles of Scotland's history. The clearing became filled with pale figures in every variety of fighting garb from chain mail of the thirteenth century to khaki shirts and shorts worn by the men of the Highland regiments who had fought in the African desert in World War II. The majority of the figures wore kilts representing nearly every clan and regiment of Scotland.

Simon Smith, who had actually fainted from sheer surprise and not fear, strode grimly into the milling throng of spirits. He picked out a bearded, kilted Highlander and slowly circled the transparent figure, mumbling to himself, while the Scottish ghost watched him suspiciously. Coming to a halt in front of the spirit, Smith passed a hand slowly through its body.

"It's impossible for you to actually exist, you know," he remarked.

"I dinna ken ye, mon," he growled. His voice was a thin, hoarse whisper.

"I mean," said the physicist, "that you can't possibly be alive."

The ghost regarded him as he might regard a very young child who has just done something foolish, "O' course I'm not alive," he said petulantly. "I'm a ghostie."

Simon pointed a finger at him. "You can't really whisper that way," he stated in a lecturing tone. "Sound is caused by vibrations emanating from a material source, and since you're supposedly a nonmaterial being, therefore you cannot make a noise. You don't even have any vocal cords. You simply cannot talk."

The ghost bared his teeth in a nasty grin. "Well, if I canna talk," he replied in his hoarse whisper, "then ye canna hear me say that yer a foolish, ignorant sassenach wi' less sense than a half-witted donkey!"

Ignoring this jibe, the physicist shoved his hands deep into his pockets and shuffled off, shaking his head and muttering. "Has to be a rational explanation. They could be gaseous, but that doesn't explain their ability to make sounds. And even if they are gaseous, there has to be a binding force to hold them together—" He sat down and began scratching an equation in the dirt near the fire.

"Fighting men of Scotland," cried Merlin in a great voice. The assemblage of ghostly eyes turned toward him.

Merlin began to speak and he weaved a spell with his words. He made the ghosts remember the joys of life; the sight of morning sunshine dappling the green leaves of of a tree with gold, the touch of a soft breeze, the taste of good food. Then he told them of the demons and their plans, and of the misery and horror that faced the world if those plans succeeded. He spoke of the great battle he wanted the ghostly army to fight, and they seemed to hear the shrill of bagpipes. "Soldiers of Scotland!" he called, and held out his hands to them. "Only you can help us! Will you fight one last battle?"

The pale figures stirred. A single, thin, whispered shout came from their ranks. "Dinna fret yersel', mon! Tell us who ye want cleaved and lead us to 'em!"

The ghosts roared their agreement in a shout like far-off waves rolling in on a seashore. Merlin bowed gravely to them. He turned and beckoned to the robot which emerged from the shadows of the cave and clanked to him through the crowd of spirits.

"Across the border in the south of England is the ring of stones known as Stonehenge," said the wizard, sweeping over the ghosts with his eyes. "If you can fight and drive off the evil spirits that guard the stones, we will be able to secure the weapon we need to defeat the demons. We will meet you then, at Stonehenge." He straddled the broom and helped the robot clamber onto it.

But instead of forming ranks and transporting themselves to the place of battle, the ghostly Scotsmen were whispering to one another in obvious agitation. Merlin stared at them.

"What are you waiting for?" he asked in some surprise.

It was a red-coated ghost of a soldier, who had fought at Waterloo, who answered him. "We canna go into battle wi' no bagpipes a'playin'," he announced in rather shocked tones.

"Aye," whispered Bonnie Dundee. "We must have a piper."

Merlin tugged at his beard. "Of course," he mumbled almost to himself. "I had forgotten how important that is to you. Very well, I shall raise the spirit of a piper. Whom shall it be?"

"The MacCrimmons are the best o' all pipers," said Bonnie Dundee.

"Och, ye never heard my cousin Duncan MacGregor," said Rob Roy. "He's the one we want."

"Nay then, 'tis Tam Farquahar o' Inch," said a barefooted and bewhiskered Highlander, whose sole garment seemed to be a kilt. "Why, he could play the pipes in a way to charm the wild boars oot o' the woods to listen."

"What aboot Ian Beg who piped for the Chisholms at Culloden?" asked another Highlander. "He piped on the ancient Black Chanter which had magical powers."

"Och, it should be Alan Davidson," insisted a ghost in the kilt of Clan Davidson. Another ghost, wearing the kilt of Clan MacPherson, turned to look at him. Unfortunately, these two clans had frequently feuded bloodily with one another.

"What would a Davidson know o' pipe music," sneered the MacPherson. "They all have donkey's ears."

In a single motion, the Davidson whipped out his claymore, and with a smooth backhand slash cut off the MacPherson's head. Since the MacPherson was a ghost, his head stayed on his shoulders, however.

"That was a foul blow!" he yelled, drawing his own claymore. "I'll pay ye back wi' a fair one."

In an instant, dirks, claymores, and broadswords were flashing in the moonlight as the ghostly army swiftly took sides. A civil war seemed imminent.

Angus, watching from the forest's edge, thought that this was the first time since he had met him, that Merlin seemed at a loss for what to do. The wizard clutched his beard and stamped his foot. "Scotsmen," he groaned. "With the fate of the world at stake, they start a brawl over who can best play an instrument that sounds like a cat having its tail pulled!"

Help suddenly appeared from an unexpected source. "ATTENTION," roared an exceptionally loud voice. It was Sergeant Major Small.

When a Scottish Sergeant Major gives a command,

the sound is like a combination of a lion roaring at the top of its lungs and a bull elephant bellowing in rage. The effect it produced was immediate. Every ghost who had ever served in a Scottish regiment snapped to attention in an instant. The other knights and warriors were so startled that they put down their weapons and stared. The Sergeant Major strode toward them, his kilt wagging and his moustache bristling fiercely above a jutting chin.

"Now then," he roared, "stop this nonsense! Call yourselves soldiers? Why you're nothing but a bunch of thick-skulled, half-witted recruits who haven't the sense to wipe your own noses! Straighten up, you!" he bellowed at a man in the uniform of the army that had fought the French in 1815. He made a grab for the man's musket, but his hand passed through it. "I'll bet that bore is filthy. When's the last time you cleaned it?"

"Aboot a hundred and fifty years ago, sir," said the man in a frightened voice.

"I thought so!" exclaimed Small. "Well, what have you to say for yourself?"

"I couldna help it, sir," said the man. "I been dead since then."

"That's no excuse!" roared Small. "Turn yourself in for punishment detail after the battle. Now then," he continued in a lower voice, "I agree ye need a piper, but ye'll no get anywhere brawlin' aboot it. So I'll just ask the wizard here to call up the five greatest pipers in Scotland's history and that settles the matter. STAND AT EASE!"

A ghostly officer, who had fought in the army of the Duke of Marlborough in 1704, turned to another who wore a uniform of the 1890's. "I guess Sergeant Majors don't change much, do they?" he remarked. "This one sounds just like the one my regiment had two hundred and fifty years ago."

"He even looks like the one my regiment had," replied the other.

So once again Merlin performed his intricate maneuvers around the guttering fire, intoned his incantation, and flung up his arms. "Let the five greatest pipers who ever dwelled in this land now waken and come forth!" he commanded.

There was a surging billow of smoke, and one at a time, five kilted figures, each carrying a set of pipes tucked under its arm, stepped out. There were whispers of satisfaction as members of the ghostly army recognized men they knew or had heard of.

"Now ye can do this properly," stated Small. "I suggest ye form ranks under the command o' Wallace and the Bruce and march at once to Stonehenge. Pipers, ye're goin' to battle in England. Give the laddies 'Blue Bonnets Oe'r the Border.' "

Expertly, the pipers tucked the bags of their instruments under their arms, threw the drones over their shoulders, and inflated the bags with deep puffs of breath. In a moment the drones began to hum, and the chanters wailed a wild, stirring march. Led by William Wallace and Robert the Bruce, the ranks of the ghostly army began to march off.

"Take us to Stonehenge," commanded Merlin, and the broom, with wizard and robot astride it, rose and soared off into the night. Simon Smith watched it go with open mouth.

"No, no!" he yelled. "They can't do that! It's impossible!"

"Ye'd better run after and tell them then," observed Angus, who had come to stand beside the fire. "They don't seem to know it," he added drily.

Simon glared at him. Rubbing out the equation on which he'd been working, which proved that ghosts could not exist, he began to work on one proving that brooms could not fly.

Chapter 11

The strange circle of huge, rectangular stones loomed dark and ominous in the moonlight which palely lit one side of each stone, leaving the other sides nearly obscured in inky blackness. For thousands of years Stonehenge had stood on this lonely plain, each of the twenty-foot tall, forty-ton columns gradually eroding and pitting with the passage of time; many finally falling down, some lying atop others. They were ancient when Arthur ruled Britain, ancient even when the Roman Legions of Caesar came to the British isles. Stonehenge is still shrouded in mystery and legend, and many of the legends are dark with blood and terror.

But there was no terror in the grim army assembled outside the ring of stones on the side away from the highway. None of these bearded, kilted, and armored men had known fear while they lived, and they certainly felt none now.

"The sword is buried in the center of the circle," said Merlin. "No mortal man can reach it while the evil spirits which dwell among these stones protect it with their spell of terror. But you who are ghosts yourselves cannot be affected by this spell. Strike out now, for the freedom of the world!"

Robert the Bruce raised his great ax. "For freedom and Bonnie Scotland," he called. Again the pipes began to shrill, and the army surged forward toward the stones.

And suddenly, hundreds of other figures appeared before the ring of stones, seeming to ooze up from the ground. They were not pale and clear as were the ghosts of the Scottish warriors, but gray and shadowy. They were the shapes of squat, long-haired men clad in black-dyed, crudely sewn robes of animal skin. Their shadowy faces were twisted with hatred, and they brandished spears tipped with sharpened stones. The force of terror and evil that pulsed forth from them was so powerful that it struck Merlin like a blow.

But it affected the Scottish ghosts not at all. With wild yells that blended into a single great whispered roar, they broke into a furious headlong charge. Both sides battled as they had when they were living, breathing men of flesh and blood. But neither side could injure the other, nor could either side tire. Swords and axes sheered through shadowy bodies, spears passed into and through pale, kilted shapes. A man can die but once, and none of the ghostly warriors in this battle could be killed by even the most terrible of blows.

So the two sides remained locked in combat, straining to force each other back. Desperately, Merlin looked at the sky. "We must win soon," he groaned, "or daylight will be upon us and our army will fade. Oh, by the blood of the Red Dragon, if only I could do something."

"Something is taking place which your senses are insufficient to observe," intoned the robot standing silver and immobile. "I perceive that the defenders of the ring of stones have been pushed back thirteen and seven-eighths inches."

Merlin knew that the robot's infallible vision and ability to compute were completely reliable. At the top of his lungs he shouted, "You're beating them, Scots! You're pushing them back!"

Merlin's yell of encouragement was the final spark that was needed. The bagpipes screamed, and with yells of triumph the Scots ghosts pushed forward. The shadowy figures were now noticeably giving ground, gnashing their teeth in rage and frustration. And abruptly, they began to vanish.

In twos and threes, then in dozens, the snarling, skin-clad figures winked out of existence. Suddenly they were all gone, and gone too, was the power that had held Merlin back.

"Come, MacHinery, quickly," called the wizard, and he sprinted into the ring of stones, passing right through the victorious Scottish ghosts. Some were milling about giving shouts of laughter and whoops of triumph in their thin, spirit voices, and many were dancing a fling to the tune of the pipes.

Reaching the very center of the ring, Merlin stopped, pointed his finger straight down toward the earth beneath his feet, and spoke a half dozen words in a strange sounding tongue. Then he cried, "Sword of Galahad, arise!"

Deep within the earth there was a rumbling. The ground shuddered and the huge stones of the circle swayed slightly. The ghosts grew silent, watching in awe. The ground at Merlin's feet split open, and a sword in a scabbard rose swiftly, hilt first, straight up out of the fissure until only a few inches of its tip remained imbedded. It was a beautiful weapon. The hilt was of ivory, carved in a winding, grooved pattern so that it would not slip in the user's hand, and the pommel was an enormous blood red ruby carved into the shape of a lion's head. The crosspiece was of steel, inlaid with gold and silver, and the scabbard was of shimmering green dragon skin, bound with gold.

Merlin glanced at the robot. "Champion, take up the Sword of Power," he said in a voice of triumph. The wind was ruffling his hair and beard, and his eyes were blazing.

The robot grasped the hilt of the sword with both hands and lifted it free of the earth, swinging it in a great arc as he did so, so that the point was aimed at the sky above. From the ground under the stones there came a faint wailing; weak but filled with anger and hatred.

"Let us move outside this cursed ring lest the shadow folk rally and attack us again," said Merlin. Swaggering and lounging indifferently, the ghosts of the victorious army also left the circle and gathered about the wizard and the robot.

Merlin appraised the grinning, kilted, and mailed figures for a moment or two. Then he placed his right hand upon his heart and bowed low in sincere respect.

"Fighting men of all ages," he said, straightening and facing them, "believe me when I tell you that you have fought one of the greatest of all your fights. I have seen many battles and watched the greatest warriors of Arthur's Round Table in combat against their foes, but I speak truly when I say that none but you could have bested the dark guardians of Stonehenge."

"Now we must fight *our* battle against the demons

and their terrible leader. You have done your part, and a great one it was, in helping us gain the weapon with which we can win."

William Wallace spoke for all. "I am glad our part was well done. Good fortune to you in yours."

Again the wizard bowed his head. Then he raised a hand, palm outward, toward the ghostly army. "And now I release you. Warriors, return to your rest," he said gently. "And the blessings and thanks of the world be with you."

Slowly, the pale figures began to fade. There were whispered shouts of "Gude luck to ye," and "Give 'em a blow for me," and then Merlin and MacHinery, holding the sword, were alone on the plain outside the circle of standing stones.

Merlin smiled. Half to himself he murmured, "And never again shall I say that a bagpipe sounds like a cat having its tail pulled." The breeze ruffled his beard and he glanced skyward. "Dawn is but a few hours away," he observed. "We must return to Maggie MacMurdoch's cave. There is still much to do and little time in which to do it."

Merlin and the robot had been gone but a few minutes when a single patch of gray fog began moving across the plain toward the circle. Oddly, it was moving against the faint breeze that blew. Reaching the stones, it flowed in among them, moving toward the very center of the ring. When it came upon the cleft in the ground from which the sword had arisen, it suddenly coiled backward, like a surprised snake. For a moment it writhed and twisted violently as though in great turmoil, even though the breeze had completely ceased to blow. Then, moving quickly, it seeped out of the ring and was lost in the darkness of the plain.

It was early morning, and the small group of demon fighters were once again gathered together in Maggie's magic room. Simon Smith once again inspected his creation, thoughtfully slid his hand up the blade of the great sword, then gazed at the wizard.

"All right, Merlin, you've got your magic sword, and MacHinery, as you persist in calling him, seems to be in perfect operating condition," he announced. "Now what?"

Merlin's eyes were red rimmed from lack of sleep, and he rubbed them wearily. "First, I must get some rest," he answered apologetically. "Then we shall have a council of war and I will explain my plans and welcome any suggestions you care to make."

"Well, I slept last night while you were out fighting ghosts," said Simon, "so I think I'll take a little walk while you're sleeping. I admit that I've seen, or I seem to have seen, some things which I still consider impossible, and I have some thinking to do."

" 'Tis not a gude day fer walkin'," remarked Angus. " 'Tis gray and foggy wi' no sign o' the sun."

"That doesn't bother me," answered Simon. "But I think better when I'm alone, and if you're all going to be snoring in here, you'll interrupt my concentration."

Merlin smiled, and tilting his chair back, closed his eyes. "Do not stray too far into the forest, friend Smith," he urged, drowsily. "In a fog, it would be easy to get lost."

"I won't," grunted the physicist, ambling toward the passageway. "Can I get back through the barrier when I want to, Mrs. MacMurdoch?"

The witch's head was nodding, for she had stayed anxiously awake all night awaiting Merlin's return. "Aye," she mumbled. "It will raise and lower for any o' us, but for no other."

Simon departed. The door swung open at his approach, which made him frown, and closed after he had passed through it. Looking back over his shoulder, he saw that the cliff wall again appeared blank. There was no sign of a door inside the shallow cave. He shook his head uncertainly.

The sky was completely overcast, and the trees at the far edge of the clearing were pale, fuzzy shapes, shrouded in gray, hanging mist. As he crossed the clearing and neared them, their outlines sharpened, and he found the path easily. He walked a short distance into the woods until he came to a fallen tree beside the path. Seating himself on this, he put his chin in his cupped hand and began to think aloud:

"I live in the twentieth century. I am educated in twentieth century technological concepts. I understand how and why things work as they do. An internal combustion engine might have seemed like magic to an ancient Greek, but he could have built an internal combustion engine, if he'd had the proper tools, because it operates on ordinary, physical laws. But a flying broom does not! Ghosts do not! There can be no such thing as a nonmaterial being because everything is composed of material—even light! Now these ghosts could have been gaseous, but then what enabled them to hold their shapes? What enabled them to talk?"

Picking up a dry, pointed twig, he bent over and began to scratch a series of equations on the bare dirt of the path. As he worked he lost all track of time. A half hour might have passed or even two hours, but suddenly a voice broke into his thoughts.

"Ye'll pardon me fer askin'," it said. "But what in the name of Auld Clootie be ye doin' there?"

With a start, Simon glanced up. Standing on the path a few feet from him was a tall, elderly man with a pleasant, wrinkled face covered with a stubble of beard and crowned with a mane of tousled gray hair. He wore a kilt, plaid stockings, and heavy walking shoes around which the white mist was curling. A bulky sweater covered his upper body, and a knapsack was strapped to his back. He leaned on a sturdy, knobbed walking stick.

"I wanted to do some thinking," said Simon, shortly. He felt like adding "by myself," but his natural good nature kept him from being rude.

"Ye'll pardon me fer askin'," said the man, eyeing him curiously, "but those be strange marks ye're makin'. Is it a furrin language?"

Simon sighed. He saw that he had a conversation on his hands with this nosey and talkative old Highlander, whether he wanted one or not. "I'm what you'd call a scientist—a physicist, to be exact. And those are called equations. They're a sort of arithmetic."

"Now that's interestin'. I never met one before. What does a fizzysist do?"

Simon did the best he could to explain. Picking up a

small stone, he threw it in an arc until it vanished into the mist. They heard it land with a thump somewhere nearby. "A physicist," said Simon carefully, "wants to know why that stone took the path it did. Why it didn't wiggle instead of sailing straight. Why it didn't just drop out of my hand. How long it will stay in the air depending on how hard you throw it."

The other scratched his chin. "What good is it to wonder about such things?"

"Because," said Simon gently, "they are problems to be solved that can help us solve other problems. Like measuring the path that the moon takes around the earth," replied Simon, knowing that this would be meaningless to the old Scotsman.

"But what good is it to know that?" asked the man.

"You can't understand," sighed Simon. "You see, I just like to know about these things. And when I bump into a problem that doesn't make sense, I can't rest until I work it out."

"Ah," said the old man. With his stick he pointed at the equations. "And what sort of problem is it that ye're tryin' to solve wi' those—eekwayshuns, did ye call 'em?"

"I was trying to prove the existence of ghosts," said Simon grimly. "But I can't, because they don't exist."

"Oh," said the Highlander. "Do ye not believe in ghosties?"

"No," replied Simon. "Well, that is, not entirely."

"Well, noo," said the old man, "ye shouldn't be too hasty aboot such things."

What happened then was so shocking that Simon was completely unprepared for it. The man reached up with two brown, gnarled hands and took his face off. The pleasant, wrinkled countenance and the tousled hair peeled away like a rubber Halloween mask. What was left was a bare, white grinning skull, with two redly gleaming points of light flickering in the black eye sockets that stared into the physicist's own horrified eyes.

"Do you believe in ghosties noo?" asked the skull. It leaned closer until the black sockets were only inches away. "Listen, mortal, you will tell me what I wish to know. Merlin is in the witch's cave, and they have the Sword, have they not? Answer!"

Simon felt as if he were in a dream, struggling to awake. All the world had turned gray, and he could see nothing but two immense black holes with glowing red sparks far down in their depths. "Yes," he heard himself answer in a faint, far away voice.

"Who is with them?"

Simon struggled to escape from his trancelike state, but to no avail. He *had* to answer. "Constable Wier. Sergeant Small. Three brownies. The robot. And me."

"Robot?" hissed the questioning voice. "What is that?"

And Smith answered honestly, "An electronic powered, servomechanism in manlike form, with a sensory system and computor brain."

"Your words have no meaning," hissed the questioner. "Is it a magical device? What does it do?"

"It is not magical," said Simon dreamily. Some part of his mind was still struggling to break free and it seemed as if, far away, someone was calling his name. "It is designed to do work."

"Two mortals, three brownies, a slave, and a fool who likes to know why the moon goes around the earth," said the voice. "Clearly I have little to fear."

There *were* other voices calling his name now. He could hear them distinctly. The world was still gray, but the black holes were gone. Suddenly the grayness vanished, and Simon found himself lying on a bed in the witch's cave gazing into the anxious, blue eyes of the wizard, Merlin.

Chapter 12

Simon struggled to sit up, but Merlin gently forced him back. "Rest yet awhile," he said. "You have suffered a harrowing experience."

"What happened?" gasped Simon.

"We were awakened by the guardian crying that an evil force was probing the barrier," Merlin replied. "As soon as it left, Sergeant Small and Constable Wier hurried out to search for you. They found you finally, lying face down in the woods beside a fallen tree, looking so drawn and gray that they feared you were dead. They carried you back here."

Simon closed his eyes. "I remember," he said weakly. "But it seems like a dream. I met an old Highlander who asked a lot of questions. Then suddenly he changed into something horrible and he asked other questions which I had to answer. I couldn't help myself!" He groaned. "It wasn't a dream, was it, Merlin? He hypnotized me didn't he? And I told him everything about us! I've ruined your plans!"

"No!" said the magician, firmly. "You have helped

them. You met Urlug, or one of Urlug's creatures, and he put you into the sleep of mind possession—hypnotism, as you call it. But I know what you told him, for I too probed your mind while you were still in the sleep. You told him exactly what MacHinery is—a machine that is designed to do work. Consequently, he thinks the robot is simply a sort of slave. He is contemptuous of Small, Wier, and the Brownies, and he believes that you are a fool who seeks answers to useless questions. Therefore, he is convinced that I will bear the Sword of Power against him. He will ignore MacHinery, and all his efforts will be aimed at me. And nothing could be better, for this gives us an even greater chance of enabling MacHinery to reach him with the Sword."

Maggie entered the room with a steaming cup cradled in her hands. "Drink this, laddie," she urged. " 'Twill help bring yer strength back."

"What is it?" grunted Simon, as Merlin slipped an arm under his head and eased him to a sitting position. "A magic potion?"

"Nay," chuckled the witch. "Just gude beef broth."

As he sipped the hot liquid, he felt the chill leave his body. His senses now seemed fully clear, so he swung his legs off the bed and onto the floor. "I think I'm all right now." Standing up, he took a few hesitant steps, then briskly walked the length of the room, "Yes, I'm fine," he announced.

"Good," said the wizard heartily. "Then come to the magic room and let us discuss our next moves."

Maggie, Merlin, and the physicist took seats at the table where Small and Wier were sitting while the three brownies sat cross-legged against one wall. MacHinery, silent and immobile as always, stood beside the bearded painting, holding the Sword upright before him. Bathsheba lay curled across his metal feet.

"Now, then," said the wizard. "The time has come for our council of war. I will outline my plan, and then any of you who have any ideas concerning it, please speak up."

"A friend of mine who was a great warrior once remarked that the best defense is a good offence. Therefore, I feel that we must invade demonland as quickly as possible."

He cleared his throat and was about to continue speaking, when the bearded painting suddenly raised its voice. "I detect many, many hostile presences gathering in the woods outside!"

There was a moment of frozen silence. Then Merlin leaped from his chair with an exclamation and peered into the murky mirror. Curious, Simon joined him.

"Too dark to see anything," muttered the wizard. "I'll make a light, but it will last for only an instant. Look carefully, Simon, and help me see what's out there."

He spoke a single word, and for just a few seconds, the clearing outside the cave was revealed in the mirror, brightly lit as though by a lightning flash. Simon gasped. The instant of illumination had shown that a horde of figures were pouring out of the forest, into the clearing. Simon caught quick impressions of scuttling, malformed shapes, clad in black scale armor, bearing shields and spears. He saw bulbous, staring eyes and cruel mouths. "Are those demons?" he asked in dismay.

"Yes!" Merlin brought his fist down upon the table with a crash that caused the stuffed raven to topple over and the crystal ball to wobble on its stand. "What a fool I am not to have anticipated that Urlug would send his forces against us now that he knows for sure where we are, and how feeble is our strength."

"But the Sword," exclaimed Maggie. "We have the champion and the Sword o' Power!"

"The Sword is only of use against Urlug," said the wizard staring about wildly, "and Urlug is not with those outside. He has no need to be. He is relying upon numbers to defeat us, not magic."

"We'll just have to fight 'em off," said Small calmly, reaching for his Sten gun.

"With my magic and your weapons and MacHinery's untiring strength, we can slay hundreds," said the wizard. "But once they break in, they will overwhelm us with sheer numbers. There are a thousand or more of them out there. Our only hope is that I can hold the barrier up until dawn."

"Why dawn?" questioned Simon, sharply.

"The demons cannot stand strong light," answered Merlin absently. "Starlight, moonlight, even torchlight, yes; but sunlight they cannot abide."

"Then all we need is a strong enough light between us and the demons, and they can't get at us," Simon declared. "OK Merlin, if you're a real magician, I can get us out of this. But if you're a fake, our goose is cooked. Listen; can you produce things? I mean, can you really conjure things up out of nowhere?"

"Of course," said the wizard. "But what—"

"No time for *buts*," snapped Simon. "Get me two round sticks of graphite about four inches long and as thick as your fingers."

"The barrier is failing," cried the painting.

Merlin turned and made a series of passes with his hands and muttered some words. Then he glanced at Simon. "What is graphite? I don't know the word."

"It's a highly compressed carbon," said Simon excitedly.

"Carbon! What is carbon?" cried the magician.

"Oh, blast it! How can I make you understand?" Simon found himself yelling. "It's a chemical element with a valence of plus or minus four and a nucleus with—"

"I don't understand!" exclaimed the magician raising his arms in vexation. "Simon, this is as unfathomable to me as one of my magical spells is to you. Can you show me this substance?" His brow was beaded with sweat.

Simon glanced around desperately, then had a sudden inspiration. "Constable Wier. Do you have a pencil?"

"Aye," said the constable, fumbling furiously in the upper pocket of his uniform tunic. "I carry one for making notes when I have to make an official report." Handing it to the physicist, he remarked somewhat abashedly, "I dinna use it much."

"Here," said Simon, holding the pencil before Merlin and touching its point with his fingertip. "This is graphite."

Merlin seized the pencil, glanced at the point, then set it down on the table. There was a tiny flash and there appeared two, finger-thick, four inch long cylinders of black shiny substance.

"That's it!" crowed Simon. "Now—copper. Do you know what copper is?"

"Yes, praise to the Red Dragon!"

"Then get me two lengths of copper wire about twice

as long as you are, and about half as thick as that pencil."

Merlin reached into the air with one hand and seemed to pluck two stands of wire from nowhere.

"The barrier! The barrier!" called the painting.

Gritting his teeth, the magician repeated his passes and mumbled words. Sweat was now pouring down his face, and his teeth were clenched.

"Now," said Simon, "I need a round shield, like the knights used. Make it about so big." He described a circle in the air with his arms. "And make it convex, like a shallow bowl, and as bright and shiny as possible. Put a hole on each side of it, just a little bit bigger than those pieces of wire."

This time Merlin muttered a few words. A shield of the exact sort Simon had described appeared out of thin air and fell to the floor with a clank. From outside the cave a dull thumping noise began.

"They must be using a batterin' ram against the side o' the cave," muttered Small, fondling his weapon.

Simon ignored him. "Now, the last thing," he said. He pulled off his battered shoe and pointed at the worn rubber heel. "Two pieces of this stuff about as thin as a piece of paper and a couple of inches square."

Merlin placed his fingertips on the rubber and closed his eyes. With his other hand he reached out once more, and from thin air plucked two pieces of rubber which he handed to the physicist. From outside, the thumping was growing louder.

"Don't worry," said Simon grabbing up the strands of wire and the sticks of graphite. "In a minute we'll have plenty of light, and a big surprise for our nasty friends out there."

With one foot shod and the other bare, Simon hurried into the passageway. "MacHinery, pick up the shield and follow me," he called. The robot leaned the great Sword against the wall, and picking up the shining shield, followed his creator from the room. The others clustered anxiously after.

"Stand here," ordered Simon, pointing to a spot a few feet from the door, "and hold the shield straight out in front of you with the inward curve facing the door."

Working feverishly, the physicist tightly wound a strand of wire around each of the graphite sticks. Then he stuffed one of the rubber squares into each of the holes on the shield's sides and slipped the wires into the holes through the rubber. He was careful that the wire was completely sheathed by the rubber and did not touch any part of the metal shield. He bent each wire inward so that the two graphite sticks pointed toward one another, a fraction of an inch apart, in the center of the shield.

"Open your frontal area," he ordered, moving around to the robot's side. Knowing that it might be necessary to make repairs on the robot's internal parts, he had constructed it so that a large section of its tubular body could be made to swing open. This section was hermetically sealed and could be activated by the robot itself. Soundlessly it now opened, revealing the intricate parts inside. Simon quickly attached one wire to a terminal within the robot's interior and the other wire to another.

After a moment or two, the ends of each of the carbon sticks began to glow. The glow quickly turned white. Then, an intense, blue white light snapped and crackled between the two sticks. The curved, shiny surface of the shield intensified the light. The inner surface of Maggie's gray wooden door turned glaring white. Simon had constructed a crude carbon arc lamp, using the same principle by which a searchlight beam operates.

"The barrier is yielding!" called the voice of the painting from the other room.

"To heck with the barrier," said Simon confidently. "Open the door!" Maggie glanced at the wizard, who nodded, his face as alight with triumph as the glow that filled the passageway. Everyone stood huddled behind the figure of the robot who stood stolidly, shield erect before him, facing the door. Slowly, it swung open.

A yell of wild triumph from a hundred demon throats burst in upon them. But it turned instantly into a prolonged scream of dismay and horror. For upon the demon soldiers clustered at the cave entrance, there shown a blinding, blasting glare of intense, blue-white light that poured out into the clearing, reaching even to the forest edge, illuminating the entire area with a brilliance more dazzling than the brightest sun.

The demons nearest the light shrieked in high-pitched, agonized voices. Their bulging eyes were blinded, and their pallid skins were reddened and blistered. Flinging down their weapons, they turned and clawed their way madly through the warriors behind them, who in turn began to fall back, blinded and terrified by the fierce light which poured mercilessly upon them. Reeling, stumbling, falling, they sought only to escape back into the blackness. They melted away from the front of the cave like leaves blown by a strong wind. Scores remained, crawling aimlessly on hands and knees, shrieking with pain and terror, burnt and blinded, unable to find their way out of the brightness.

Merlin heaved a shuddering sigh and wiped his brow with the sleeve of his robe. "How long will this light burn, Simon?" he asked.

"Long enough," said the physicist. "Fortunately, the nights are short in this part of the world because we're so close to the Arctic Circle. The carbon will be used up eventually, but I'm sure morning will be here before then."

"Then we are saved," said the wizard simply. "I don't understand how you did it. It is greater than any feat of magic I could perform."

Simon looked at him squarely. "Merlin, I could never have constructed this without the materials you provided from wherever you got them. I don't understand how you did that, but," he grinned, "we sure make a heck of a good team."

The wizard returned his grin. "We do indeed. But I still say that you deserve the lion's share of the credit."

Angus was shielding his eyes and peering out from behind MacHinery's knee. The clearing was perfectly empty; even the blinded, crippled demons had managed to crawl away into the safety of the dark woods. "They're all gone," he announced. "Shall we continue the council o'war?"

"The council, I think, is over," remarked Merlin. "I think there can be no doubt now but that we must carry the battle to Urlug at once. I think we should use the rest of the night for sleeping, and tomorrow we shall set out to join the rest of our army. And tomorrow night we invade demonland."

"Our army?" said Simon. "I didn't know we had one. Who are they?"

"Do you recall when I told you of the first great war

fought ages ago against the demons?" asked the wizard. "And of the race of dwarves who joined in conquering them? Well, less than four hours walk from here is the last great stronghold of the dwarves—the city of Glamoreth which lies in a hidden cavern in the deeps of Mount Moraigh. Fortunately, as I learned from Angus, the dwarves have kept sharp eyes upon the demons even through all the ages that have passed. It was they who first learned that the demons were growing in strength and hungering once more for power."

"Aye," chimed in Angus. " 'Twas their Chieftain, Gwedhedda, who told me to seek oot Maggie and ask her what might be done. And 'twas Maggie who had the idea to free Merlin, and sent us oot to search for a knight. And after months o' searchin', we found Sir MacHinery in yer castle. The rest, ye know."

"Well, I've slept enough today," said Simon wryly, "so I'll keep watch here with MacHinery, just in case, while the rest of you sleep."

So while the others trooped off, Simon sat down with his back against the passageway wall and awaited the coming of dawn. The robot, still firmly holding the shield from which the light flared forth into the clearing, stood immobile.

Despite his protestations, Simon's head began to nod, and Merlin, awakening with the morning dawn, found him slumped down in the passageway, snoring lustily. "Awaken, Great Maker of Bright Lights!" he boomed. "We must breakfast and then be off."

Simon rubbed his eyes. "Guess I'm not much of a sentry," he commented. "Good thing MacHinery doesn't sleep."

Rising, he disconnected the wires from the two terminals within the robot's body. "Close yourself up," he ordered, and the robot's frontal plate swung shut with a faint thump and resealed itself. "Put the shield down." MacHinery dropped the shield with a clank that made them wince and woke up everyone else in the cave.

After a simple breakfast of oatcakes and tea, they prepared to leave. Sergeant Major Small checked his Sten gun and his bag of ammunition. Constable Wier adjusted his helmet and grumbled a bit because he had no razor, and his chin had become stubbly with whiskers. The robot, without being told, picked up the great Sword, and Maggie fondly caressed her favorite magical possessions. "Keep an eye on things," she told the bearded painting.

"Good luck," it said with a choke in its bass voice. Simon was only mildly surprised to see a tear trickle down its painted cheek and into its beard.

They passed through the door which swung shut after them. It did not, to Simon's surprise, vanish and turn into bare rock, but Merlin, noting his expression, explained. "No need for a barrier any longer," he said. "If we are successful, we shall return. If not," he shrugged, "there will be no haven anywhere for anyone."

"By yer leave, sir," said Sergeant Small addressing the wizard, "I think we should observe proper military procedure. I'll move oot first, as the point—the advance guard that is—wi' Angus to show me the way. Ye other two brownies move oot to the right and left aboot fifty yards as flank guards, and if anyone tries to come at us from the side, yell oot! Merlin, Maggie, Professor Smith, and the robot will be the main force, and Constable Wier can act as rear guard to make sure no one sneaks up on us from behind. All right, let's move, oot!"

Merlin chuckled as the burly, kilted figure strode off, Sten gun at the ready. "He reminds me so much of Lancelot," he said. "Lance was never one to be caught off guard, either."

Simon eyed him curiously. "There's not much doubt in my mind any more that you really are Merlin," he acknowledged. "So tell me; what sort of a man was King Arthur?"

"That's a remarkable thing too," said the wizard with a sidelong glance at him. "He was very, very much like you. He never quite believed that my magic was real, and he was always trying to find out what made things work. I found him once with a bucket full of water to which he had tied a rope. He was swinging it around his head in a circle. 'Look, Merlin,' he said to me. 'You'd think the water would slop out, but it doesn't! Something holds it in when I swing it fast like this. What could it be?' He was very interested and excited."

Simon smiled. "Sounds as though he had the makings of a physicist," he commented. "Wish I'd been there, I could have explained it to him. Could you?"

Merlin laughed, ruefully. "That was one of those problems that I struggled to solve for many days," he admitted. "I finally decided that some kind of force was exerted which pushed the water into the pails."

"You were pretty close," grinned Simon. "We call it centrifugal force. A rotating object tends to move away from the center of its rotation."

"Now that," said the magician, "like your explanation of carbon last night, sounds as strange to me as one of my incantations does to you." He glanced again at the physicist. "Yes, you are very much like him, even to the look in your eyes. You know, I foretold that both he and I would return when the world had greatest need of us. This seems to be the time, and here am I, but I guess I was wrong about him. However, you've taken his place Simon. You saved us from the demons last night, and your invention of the robot may well be the salvation of the world."

Simon faltered in his stride and nearly stumbled. He had just realized something. It should have been obvious, but it had just not occurred to him until Merlin spoke. Simon had never liked his first name because it had seemed sissified to him as a little boy, and as he grew older he used his middle name, Simon, instead. He had done this for so long that he had almost forgotten that his real first name was Arthur.

Chapter 13

The little group trudged along, each member immersed in his own thoughts. As nearly as Simon could judge, they were following a course alongside the mountain which housed Maggie's cave, moving in an upward direction at a right angle to the path that led back to Strathgow. They had been walking for nearly an hour. Pine trees hemmed them on all sides, but glancing up, Simon could see the peak of the mountain rising stark and bare, above and slightly behind them. About fifty yards ahead, the figure of Sergeant Small was visible, striding cautiously along the path as though he momentarily expected an ambush. Angus was perched on his left shoulder. There was no sign of the other two brownies flitting through the woods on either side. Fifty yards to the rear Constable Wier paced stolidly along, hands clasped behind his back. Every twenty paces or so, he turned and peered suspiciously along the path that stretched out behind them.

Maggie, using her broom as a walking stick, was hobbling along at a remarkable pace. Bathsheba prowled sinuously at her side. That the old woman was deep in thought was evident by the fact that she was frowning darkly and touching her nose with the tip of her tongue. Abruptly she sighed and tugged at Merlin's sleeve to attract his attention. "I been thinkin'," she stated. "From what we know, the demons can probably muster an army o' thousands, can they not?"

"I would guess so," replied the wizard.

"And the dwarves are the last o' their kind," mused the witch. "Their numbers have dwindled o'er the centuries, as men have spread oot through the world. How many warriors d'ye think they can furnish?"

"Probably," said Merlin calmly, "no more than a few hundred."

"That's as I thought. It'll no be much o' an army wi' which we're invadin' demonland. A few hundred dwarves, perhaps a hundred brownies—and stout-hearted though they be, they're not but a foot tall—and the six o' us. I know we have the perfect champion in Sir MacHinery, and I know we can count on great help from your magic and a bit from mine. But Urlug has his magic too, and the demons will still ootnumber us hundreds to one!"

Merlin rubbed his forehead. "In all truth, Maggie MacMurdoch, it is not an army we are taking into demonland. It is simply a bodyguard for Sir MacHinery. I am hoping that Urlug will believe that we actually are trying to conquer him and all his demons, by means of my magic, and with the help of all the dwarves and brownies we could gather. I truly hope he is scornful of our little force. For our strength lies not in the axes of the dwarves, nor the dirks of the brownies, nor even in my magic. It lies there." He pointed at the robot, stomping methodically along with the great broadsword held rigidly before it. “And should every one of us perish, if he can but reach Urlug and smite him, the battle is won!”

“Even so,” said the witch, “should the demons attack our tiny force wi’ all their thousands o’ soldiers, they may well o’ercome us before MacHinery can use the sword. It could have happened last night but for the quick wits o’ Professor Smith. I think we need more numbers to add to our army.”

“Speak on,” said Merlin.

“The animals o’ the woods,” said Maggie. “The foxes who can see in the dark, can slip ahead and worn o’ ambush. The wildcats will fight wi’ fury! I know them, Merlin. They have no great love for men, but they live in peace wi’ dwarf and brownie and Maggie MacMurdoch. In their own way, they too know o’ the danger from the demons. They will help us Merlin. And they will make our numbers greater.”

“It is a good thought,” agreed the wizard. His eyes strayed to the cat who returned his gaze with yellow, unblinking eyes. “I presume that your feline friend here will carry our message of need to them?”

“Aye,” nodded the witch. “Bathsheba knows them all and can speak wi’ them. Bathsheba, lass, go and gather as many o’ the beasties as ye can. Have them meet us at the mountain by sundoon tonight.”

The cat yawned nonchalantly, then bounded from the path and into the woods with a burst of incredible speed.

“A most worthy beast,” commented Merlin.

“Ye can depend on her,” said Maggie, matter-of-factly. She glanced at Simon with a glint of humor in her ancient eyes. “I’m surprised that ye have nothin’ to say aboot my cat bein' able to talk to other animals, Professor Smith."

Simon shrugged. "It's unusual but not impossible," he observed. "Many animals have a great deal more intelligence than people give them credit for. A dog can understand several hundred words. Monkeys have an entire language. So do dolphins. And scientists are even learning to talk to them. Anyway," he shook his head, "nothing surprises me anymore! Half the things that have happened to me in the last few days are completely impossible, but I can't deny that they happened."

"Well, if it comes to that," said Merlin seriously, "I can scarcely believe some of the things which you have done. When I look at this mechanical marvel of yours, upon which rests our entire hope of winning this struggle, and when I think of the amazing thing you did last night. —Believe me, if you think that I am not awed by your abilities, you are very wrong."

"When this is all over—if we live through it," replied Simon, "I want to sit down and spend about two weeks just talking to you. I can explain everything I've done so that you can understand it, I'm sure. But I've got to find out how you're able to do the things you do, or I'll spend the rest of my life worrying about it."

"I would relish two weeks, or two months, of pure conversation with you, Simon," answered the wizard, sincerely.

They trudged on and soon found themselves in a barren, rocky wilderness on the slope of a mountainside. Simon had a sudden glimmer of understanding of what the Scottish Highlands really were. From their present position they could look back and see the forest sprawling down the mountainside like an immense, irregularly-shaped carpet of dark green. Far below, the forest encountered the hills, and the hills sloped off into glens in which an isolated village, such as Strathgow, might be found. But here they were among the mountains, remote, unpeopled, and arrogant in their towering pride. These were the mountains of the northland; sculptured monoliths of antiquity. "What is that," asked Simon, pointing to a vast dim shape which towered in the distance.

"That be Canisp," replied Maggie. " 'Tis one o' the taller mountains hereaboots."

"And where is this Mount Moraigh? Shouldn't we be reaching it soon?"

"Och, compared to Canisp or Suilven, Moraigh is just a wee hill," said Maggie deprecatingly. "There it lies before us."

With Angus instructing him, Sergeant Small was picking his way along an indistinct, pebble-strewn path directly toward a looming wall of ribbed rock less than a half mile away. Within twenty minutes, the entire party had reached it.

"How do we get in?" queried Simon. "Another magic door?"

"Merely a very cleverly concealed one," answered Merlin. "The dwarves are exceedingly fine craftsmen."

"How do they know we're here? Should we knock or something?"

"D'ye see that wee crevice aboot twenty feet above us?" Angus spoke up from the Sergeant's shoulder. " 'Tis a guard window. They'll have been watchin' us for some time noo, and—ah!"

A rectangular crack appeared in the rock, and as

they watched, it ponderously, but soundlessly, swung inward. The immense door of stone, nearly three feet in thickness, revealed a cobblestone courtyard brightly illuminated by flaring torchlight. And Simon had his first look at members of the great and ancient race of dwarves.

He was surprised. He had somehow assumed that, like the brownies, they would be tiny creatures, but the row of figures drawn up in line facing them from beyond the doorway were, on an average, about five feet tall and broadly proportioned. They looked like short Vikings. The long hair that fell to their shoulders and the square-cut beards that adorned their chins were uniformly fair, ranging in color from the palest blonde to reddish gold. They wore finely wrought tunics of silvery scale armor and horned, silver helmets. Their pointed-toed, high boots were of fawn colored leather, tooled with intricate designs. Each of them carried a heavy, double-bladed ax.

A few paces in front of them stood a dwarf, around whose neck hung a massive gold chain which glinted redly in the firelight. Touching his hand to his forehead, he bowed and spoke in a tongue which sounded to Simon vaguely like Welsh. It had a liquid, almost musical sound.

"He says, 'Enter Glamoreth as friends,' " interpreted Angus. And they passed through the thick stone portal into the domain of the dwarves.

Chapter 14

They found themselves in a great courtyard, closed in on all sides by stone walls chiseled and polished to a glossy smoothness. Huge wrought iron torches, each as tall as Merlin, who was the tallest person present, lined the side walls at six foot intervals, illuminating the courtyard. At the far end of the cobblestone floor, a short flight of stone steps led up to a great arched doorway around which was chiseled a delicate pattern of entwined leaves. High above this doorway, running the length of the wall was a row of tiny slits where dwarf archers could fire down upon anyone who entered the courtyard unasked. The dwarf officer headed for the steps, and from behind them came a muffled thud as the huge stone door swung back into place, sealing the mountainside.

They moved up the steps and through the arched doorway. A massive stone bridge stretched some fifty yards toward another, larger arch from which light blazed. Below them, Simon heard the sound of rushing water and glancing upward saw a roof filled with slits like those he had noted on the wall outside. He guessed that if anyone managed to locate and penetrate the immense door in the mountainside, the dwarves could seal off the archway through which they had just passed and defend the courtyard with arrow fire. Should the enemy force the archway, the drawbridge would no doubt be pulled up, and the enemy would have to cross a turbulent, fifty-foot wide moat under a hail of arrows. Obviously, the dwarves were well determined to protect and defend their last stronghold. He wondered drily, if they had ever heard of high explosives.

Traversing the drawbridge, they passed through the large portal and beheld the city of Glamoreth. From Simon, Small, and Constable Wier came simultaneous gasps of awe.

The city that lay within the enormous cavern was as much an extension of the stone around and above it as a leaf is an extension of a tree. Stalactites and stalagmites had grown together, joining floor and ceiling, and had been chiseled into fantastic pillars or corner pieces of buildings, wound round with carved stone flowers in which were centered precious and semiprecious stones. Dips and rises in the cavern floor had been carved into steps. The buildings seemed to fit and follow the configuration of the entire cavern. Their colors and shapes were contrived to blend into a mass of beauty. City and cavern were one; a glorious sculpture which could only have been created by a people to whom the stone of earth was a beloved thing of beauty.

The dwarf officer led them down a street that was made of intricately inlaid square and rectangular polished stones. In the blaze of the numerous torches which jutted forth from every pillar, it was like walking across a muted rainbow which had been shattered into fragments and lay upon the ground. Through an arched doorway of pure white alabaster they entered the great hall of the Chieftain of the Dwarves.

At least a hundred yards in length, it rose to a vaulted ceiling, crossed by beams of carved stone from which hung a score of silver chandeliers, each blazing with half a hundred candles. Rich tapestries scattered with blue sapphires sparkled in the radiance of the candlelight. The floor was silver. Standing beside a large, circular table of white, rose-mottled marble was a single, imposing figure.

His head was thrown back, not in arrogance, but proudly, as he looked at them out of pale blue eyes. A circlet of rubies crowned his head, and his hair and beard, which had once been pale blond, were snow-white with age. But he stood ramrod straight, his sturdy legs planted in a wide stance.

"I am Gwedhedda," he said simply, in a deep, powerful voice.

"And I am Merlin," said the wizard in his own deep tone. Simultaneously, they bowed to one another.

"We heard that you were free, Great Merlin," said the Chieftain, "and have been expecting you. Maggie and Angus I know, but who are these others?"

Simon became suddenly and painfully aware of his tangled beard and disreputable clothes. Amidst all this magnificence, he felt that he must look like a ragged beggar.

"These two," said Merlin, indicating Sergeant Major Small and Constable Wier, "are two brave mortals who wish to join us in our fight. And this," he pointed at Sir MacHinery, "is the champion who holds the weapon that can destroy the power of the demons."

Gwedhedda looked at the robot for some time. "He is not a flesh and blood creature," he commented at last. "Is he a magical creation of yours, Merlin?"

"No," answerd the magician and pointed to Simon. "He is a creation of this man's craftsmanship. He is a machine that can walk, and talk, and think like a man. His strength is limitless, he is untiring, he is clever, he is fearless and incorruptible. No man, dwarf, nor demon can match his prowess."

The dwarf studied the robot again. "Can you truly think like a man?" he asked.

"No," replied the robot in his flat monotone. "I think as a machine because I am a machine, not a man. A man often mixes his thinking with emotion and becomes confused. I have no emotion, therefore I think more logically than does a man."

Gwedhedda raised an eyebrow in surprise. "A most wise answer," he remarked. He pointed at the massive marble table by his side. "Can you lift this table?"

The robot shifted the sword to one hand and placed the other beneath the center of the table. With no effort whatsoever, he lifted it to the height of the dwarf's head, then gently lowered it again.

"It would have taken at least three dwarves using both hands to do that," commented Gwedhedda. He looked at Simon. "What is your name, craftsman?"

"Er—Simon Smith, sir," said the physicist, unconsciously smoothing his hair with one hand and brushing at his soiled sweatshirt with the other.

"We dwarves are the greatest craftsmen of the world," said Gwedhedda matter-of-factly, "yet no dwarf in all our thousands of years of history could have created so wondrous a thing as this. I bow to your skill."

Then he smiled, causing a host of tiny creases to appear at the corner of each blue eye. "I perceive that you are concerned over your appearance. You need not be. We judge a craftsman by what he does, not how he looks. Still, it is an easy matter to have you shaven and shorn and fitted with suitable raiment if this will make you more comfortable." He spoke a few words to the officer who was standing behind the little group. The dwarf came forward and touched Simon's shoulder. Somewhat uncertainly, the physicist followed him from the room.

"Now," said Gwedhedda abruptly, "what is your plan?"

"You know of Urlug?" asked Merlin in reply.

The dwarf's face grew grim, and his lips became a thin line. "We do."

"Well my plan is simply to gather all the warriors you can muster and march at once to the Mountain of the Demonbane, so that we may reach it before sunset tonight."

"So soon?" exclaimed Gwedhedda.

"It must be!" Merlin's eyes bored into those of the dwarf. "The demons have been loosed already. They attacked us at Maggie's cave last night, and had it not been for the skill and wisdom of Simon, we would have been overcome. But we cannot risk another such encounter. We must carry the battle to Urlug. Our only hope is for our champion to reach him and smite him with the Sword of Power!"

Gwedhedda stared at the robot. "Can he really win through and do this thing?" he wondered.

"*Only* he can do it," insisted Merlin. "When we move against Urlug, we will encounter not only his demon warriors, but his magic and his guile. I do not fear the spears of the demons or the magic of Urlug so much as I fear his ability to tempt and corrupt and ensnare. But MacHinery is a machine, Gwedhedda; he cannot be turned aside by temptations of any kind, nor by fear. He knows that his purpose is to destroy Urlug and he will let nothing stand in the way of that purpose . . . no temptation, no fear, no grief, no uncertainty. But Urlug knows nothing of this. And that is why we must attack now, lest he somehow learn that this man of metal is the thing he should fear most of all."

The dwarf nodded and strode to the wall where he gave the tasseled bellpull a sharp tug. At the far end of the hall a silver-armored dwarf officer appeared and bowed.

"Muster the warriors," said Gwedhedda. "We march within the hour."

Chapter 15

The Mountain of the Demonbane rose out of a patch of pine forest that stretched bleakly away on all sides into the dusk. The sun had dropped from sight and the pale slice of moon spilled its sparse light onto a flat, horseshoe-shaped clearing. On the grayness of the mountainside that faced onto this clearing was a patch of velvet black that marked the entrance to a cave.

There was a great throng in the clearing and among the trees on the mountain. In row upon row stood the war band of the dwarves, three hundred strong. Once, before the history of mankind had even begun, their proud race could have mustered an army of thousands.

The animals of the forest had answered the call carried to them by the witch's cat. Scores of bright-eyed foxes sat on their haunches with lolling tongues. Two dozen wildcats grumbled and sniffed suspiciously at the smell of the men present, but were ready to hurl themselves with terrifying ferocity upon any demon they might encounter.

No less than a hundred brownies were there, under

the command of Angus. Tiny enough to be able to ride upon the foxes, like a man upon a horse, they carried needle-pointed dirks no more than a few inches in length.

In the center of this oddly assorted force stood Merlin, Maggie, the robot, the two Scotsmen, and Simon Smith. Simon was utterly transformed. The barber had merely clipped, combed, and trimmed until the physicist's untidy tangle of beard, moustache, and hair had been neatly transformed in keeping with dwarf standards. A shoemaker, working with amazing speed, had produced a pair of soft leather boots which fit his feet more comfortably than any shoes he had ever worn. A tailor, with equal dexterity, had stitched together two dwarf cloaks to create a robelike garment which hung gracefully to the tops of the boots. When he had reappeared among his friends, there had been much jocular comment. Maggie told him he was 'a handsome laddie;' Sergeant Small observed that he looked like 'an auld time Scottish lord;' and the constable had likened him to the Lord Mayor of Edinburgh. Merlin had no comment, but merely stared at the physicist with deep intensity. And all during the march to the mountain, he had felt the wizard's eyes upon him.

"Very well, let us be at it," said Merlin. "Dwarves, light your torches."

Down the line of dwarves there were snappings and showers of sparks as every third warrior applied flint and steel to resin-soaked tree branches. In ever increasing numbers, the torches flared upon the grim faces and silver armor of their bearers, until finally, a long line of flickering points of light wound down the mountainside and into the forest.

Merlin turned to the small silver figure beside him.

"MacHinery," the wizard said in a low voice, "the sole purpose of the journey we are now to begin is to bring you within reach of Urlug, so that you may smite him with that sword. I can not tell you how he will appear. He may take his usual form, which is a great, curling smokelike cloud. He may appear as an ordinary demon. He may even take the shape of one of us—me or Simon or a dwarf. But I think you will know him by his actions. If you are attacked by anyone or anything, you must fight to continue on your way. If anyone, even Simon or I, should order you to stop, you must ignore the order, for it will be a trick. You must reach Urlug and strike him with the sword. That is your purpose!"

"I understand and will comply," the robot replied in his usual impassive tone. He was neither frightened, nor excited, nor even concerned. He was a machine.

"Come then," said Merlin, and headed toward the black maw in the side of the cliff. Simon walked beside him, and with measured tread, the robot came behind, the witch hobbling by his side with her cat, and Small and Wier at the rear. The animals flocked about them, and with rustlings and clankings of weapons and armor, the dwarves and brownies followed.

To the humans, black inky shadows seemed to flicker and flee before them, as the wavering torches moved through the opening and into the cave; but to Sir MacHinery and the animals, the inside of the cave was fully visible. The tiny army was entering a rapidly widening tunnel. For several minutes, marked by sounds which rang hollowly in the muffling stillness, they moved through the small cavern. Then the passage began to grow narrower until it came to a dead end. A few feet from the blank wall was a rectangular opening in the floor, which reached into blackness so intense that it seemed almost solid. A draft of cool air poured up from it.

They halted, crowding together in the narrow space. Gwedhedda came forward and stood staring at the opening with somber eyes. "So this is Demonbane, the door that opens to the bottom of the world," he mused. "Often have I heard of it in the legends of my people, but never did I think to look into it."

"It was sealed with great magic and opened with great magic," said Merlin, grimly. "Urlug's." Taking a torch from the nearest dwarf, he stooped and held it over the opening. The flickering light revealed a portion of stone stairway leading steeply down into the darkness.

"There may be a thousand demons waitin' doon there to jump us," observed Sergeant Major Small. "Why don't I just spray a clip doon those stairs and see what happens?" He patted his Sten gun.

"That'll make a heck of a racket," objected Simon. "I think we should move as quietly as possible for as long as we can."

"I agree," said Merlin. "Urlug will be aware of our presence all too soon. Let us send the foxes forward. They are small and can move silently. If there is an ambush ahead, they can warn us."

Maggie spoke a few soft words and the foxes slipped lithely and quietly into the opening. The army waited silently until a fox head emerged from the opening and emitted a series of soft yaps. "The way is clear for as far as they can see," interpreted Maggie.

"Torchbearers," commanded Gwedhedda, and several dozen dwarves came forward holding blazing brands, accompanied by other dwarves with drawn bows and arrows nocked and ready. In small groups, one torch-bearer and two archers in each, they wordlessly moved through the portal and down the steps. "First company of axmen," said Gwedhedda, and fifty dwarves with their gleaming two-headed axes at the ready, followed, accompanied by a small number of torchbearers. "I think the wildcats should go next," said Gwedhedda, "then we and the sword bearer, and behind us, the rest of the army."

"I agree," said the wizard, "but I think it most important that we have someone stay here on guard, to keep the opening free. Urlug may send demons to block it off, so we had best leave a sizeable force. Angus, you and your brownies remain here and guard the portal."

Old Angus looked sharply at the wizard. "I want a word wi' ye in private, Great Merlin," he announced. His tone was distinctly pugnacious. The wizard stepped aside and bent his head.

"Ye canna fool me," hissed the old brownie angrily. "Ye're simply tryin' to keep us oot o' the battle!"

The magician looked the tiny man squarely in the face. "You are absolutely right," he admitted. "I know your brownie warriors have great courage, but face the facts, Angus—you are less than a quarter the size of a demon, and those tiny dirks of yours would have no more effect than a pin prick. Angus, you brownies have done more than your share in this matter by finding Sir Mac-Hinery. Besides, we really do need a force here to guard the opening."

Angus hitched up his belt, morosely. "I canna deny what ye say," he admitted, bitterly. "They'll stay here then. But I go along wi' ye. And ye canna stop me. Even if ye say no, I'll just sneak along behind. I've been in this from the beginnin', and I'll see it through to the end!"

Merlin smiled. "I will not say no to you, Chieftain of the Brownies," he said respectfully. "And I speak the truth when I say that I welcome your presence with us."

Much mollified, Angus swaggered back to the portal. "I'm goin' on wi' the others," he told his warriors. "But ye must stay here and guard the door. If we be successful, we'd best find it still open when we return. Gowrie, ye're in command. No matter what happens, hold on here and keep this portal free."

With looks of resignation, frowns of chagrin, and a few expressions of relief, the brownies stood and watched as the army filed past them, through the portal Demonbane, down the stone stairway, into the darkness of the underground world of the demons.

Chapter 16

The army found itself moving down a steep, rough-hewn stairway that was closed in on both sides by irregular rock walls. To Sir MacHinery time meant nothing, but to the others it soon seemed as though they had been trudging down endless stairs in endless darkness for hours. Glancing back, they could see the portal through which they had come, glowing in the light of the torches held by the brownies left on guard. Each time they looked back, the glow seemed smaller and higher until at last it was nothing more than a pinpoint of light. Finally, it could no longer be seen at all. Still they moved downward.

When the torches had burned nearly two-thirds of their length, Gwedhedda called for a halt in a hoarse whisper that was passed along from front to rear. From their belts, the torchbearers drew new lengths of resin-smeared wood, and used their guttering brands to ignite these. As new flames flared, the old torches were dropped and ground out against the stone steps. Then the army again resumed its descent.

After another long length of time had passed, Simon

touched Merlin's shoulder. Far below, ahead of them, the torches were fanning out, no longer moving in a single file. "That must be the end of the stairway," he muttered. "It must lead into a cavern." The magician grunted in assent.

In five minutes more, they too had reached the foot of the stairs. Behind them the dwarves moved down off the steps and formed long ranks. The masses of torches coming together revealed a great cavern, studded with stalactites and stalagmites, the walls and ceiling of which were so far apart that they were well outside the torches glow and hidden in darkness. Cautiously, the army began to move forward once again and, after another long period of time had elapsed, Simon again touched Merlin's shoulder and pointed. Ahead of them, the torches of the advance party had halted and were clustered together.

"MacHinery," said Simon, knowing that the robot's vision both in darkness and for distance was amazingly sharp, "can you tell what's going on up there?"

"They have come to the entrance of a tunnel," replied the robot.

"Why do they not enter it?" wondered Gwedhedda.

"The foxes have entered," said Sir MacHinery. "I surmise that the dwarves await to see if all is safe."

"Let us continue forward," suggested Merlin.

Almost as he spoke, dozens of foxes came racing out of the tunnel and clustered about the witch and Bathsheba. There was a staccato of soft yipping barks. Maggie turned to the others. "The tunnel is short, wi' two bends in it," she said, "and it opens onto another big cavern. The foxes say there be a force o' many demons lyin' in wait for us at the tunnel's end."

"They plan to surprise us as we emerge into the

cavern, eh," said the wizard. "Well, I think we shall surprise them, instead. This is work for the wildcats. They can move sliently and fall suddenly upon the demons. Gwedhedda, have your dwarves follow closely, and when we hear the sound of the wildcats attacking, your axmen can rush forward and help."

"What aboot me?" asked Sergeant Major Small eagerly.

"I want to keep those fearsome weapons of yours a secret for a while," replied Merlin. "We may have need of other surprises. Maggie, tell the cats what they must do."

Maggie spoke a few words in the tongue of the animals to a lean wildcat. It grunted, and suddenly hundreds of shapes sprang swiftly and silently into the tunnel.

"After them, quickly," Gwedhedda hissed to his dwarves. "Move as silently as you can."

Hefting their axes, the dwarves poured into the tunnel. As they rounded the first bend, there was a sudden chorus of terrified shrieks, mingled with yelps and snarls from the tunnel's end."Forward!" yelled the Dwarf Chieftain, and his war band pelted into action. Merlin, Simon, and the others hurried after them. There were more shouts and screams from ahead.

At the tunnel's end, where it opened out onto a large cavern, there was a scene of carnage. A force of demons, nearly a thousand strong, had been drawn up silently, ready to charge the intruders the instant the torches of the dwarves appeared. But instead, hundreds of snarling, wildcats had come rushing out of the darkness and leaped, rending and tearing into the demon ranks. An instant later the three hundred dwarves had poured into the fray. The bulk of the demons had fled instantly in wild panic;

the few who stayed to fight were pulled down by the wildcats or dispatched by the axes of the dwarves. More than a hundred of the misshapen creatures lay dead, bloody and mangled. Only three wildcats had been killed, so sudden and surprising had been their onslaught.

"I think Urlug expected an easy and perhaps final victory here, but the victory is ours," said Merlin, viewing the dead demons with grim satisfaction. "Maggie, tell the animals that they have done well."

"This is easier than I thought," observed Gwedhedda complacently. "At this rate, we'll have this nest cleaned out in no time."

"No!" said Merlin sharply. "You have seen nothing yet. Urlug made a mistake, as I hoped he might, but now he will begin to rely more upon magic and guile than ordinary warfare. This was only a skirmish, Chieftain. Much worse lies ahead, you may be sure."

He had no more than finished, when there appeared at the far end of the cavern, from wall to wall and ceiling to floor, a single sheet of roaring flame, over a hundred feet in height. In horror, Simon saw that it was moving across the floor toward the army.

Silhouetted against the glare, running in terror from this, their greatest fear and enemy, came the tiny shapes of the fox scouts. They streaked past and through the lines of the dwarf soldiers. In an instant they were joined by the wildcats, rushing in blind panic through the tunnel from which they had just come; their one thought to reach the stairs and flee into the open. Infected by their panic, many of the dwarves began to surge backward with yells of fright.

"Wait!" shouted Merlin in an agonized voice. "I can stop it!"

He threw up his arms and shouted out a string of unintelligible words. There was a great peal of what sounded like thunder, and suddenly a driving, torrential downpour of rain rushed against the wall of fire. There was a tremendous hiss, a cloud of steam boiled up whitely, and the fire was gone.

The shaken army began to reform, the dwarves talking nervously and excitedly among themselves. Merlin sat down crosslegged upon the stone floor and wiped his brow with the sleeve of his robe. "The second battle goes to Urlug," he said bitterly. "At one blow he has deprived us of our animal scouts and fighters."

"What will we do now without the foxes to tell us what lies ahead?" questioned Gwedhedda in a worried voice.

"MacHinery can see as well and as far in the dark as any animal," Simon told him. "Send a few torchbearers and archers ahead a short distance. We'll follow their torches, and if MacHinery sees any danger to them, we can quickly call them back."

Gwedhedda gathered a few dozen warriors together. "Stay in groups of five—one torchbearer, two archers, two axmen," he told them. "Keep intervals of about fifty paces between each group, and stay no more than a hundred paces ahead of us. And listen well, lest the robot call you back suddenly."

The groups moved forward, and when they were some hundred paces ahead, the remainder of the force followed cautiously.

"What next, I wonder?" muttered Angus, watching the torches that twinkled in the distance.

"Almost anything, and none of it very nice," said

Merlin a trifle maliciously. "But you insisted on coming along with us, did you not?"

"Aye," said the old brownie, defiantly thrusting his chin forward, "and I'll keep going till the end, whatever it be."

Chapter 17

As they moved ahead once more, they could better see this new cavern in which they had first beaten a demon army and then been attacked by Urlug's magic wall of fire. It seemed wider than the cavern through which they had previously passed, but not as long. Ahead of them, the torches of the advance parties were drawing together once more.

"What is it, MacHinery?" asked Simon. "Another tunnel?"

"Yes," replied the robot.

When they reached it, they found it to be much narrower than the last tunnel had been. The dwarves were able to walk only two abreast and had to straggle out somewhat so that the men carrying torches would not burn those ahead of them. It was a long tunnel, and soon the entire army filled its length. Without altering his mechanical stride, MacHinery observed, "There is a vibration taking place in the rock around us."

"Wait," called Merlin. The army halted and looked apprehensively about.

"I feel it too," said Simon. Gradually, everyone became aware that the rocky ground beneath their feet was trembling ever so slightly, but with growing intensity.

"Urlug is using an earth-shaking spell to cause this tunnel to cave in and bury us," said Merlin in a strangely calm voice. "I can counter the spell, but it requires great effort. All of you run for the end of the tunnel as swiftly as you can. Move!"

The ground was shivering noticeably now, and the walls were vibrating. Small bits of rock cracked loose from the ceiling and fell with sharp impacts. Merlin walked along, his arms making sinuous intertwining motions and his lips moving silently. Dwarves squeezed past him, rushing desperately to be free of the tunnel before it collapsed upon them. Sergeant Small had hold of Maggie's elbow and was hurrying her along as best he could. Wier had picked up Angus and was sprinting down the tunnel for all he was worth. MacHinery, having been ordered to run, was well ahead of all the others. Only Simon held back, continuing to walk a few paces ahead of the magician, watching him over his shoulder. He felt strangely calm.

With terrible sounds of cracking and rending, the walls began to fall inward, the ceiling split into great chunks, the floor began to billow. There were shouts of terror from the dwarves still in the tunnel.

But then, as though cut by a knife, all sounds of rending rock, all motion of falling stone ceased. Great chunks of the ceiling, in the very act of falling, hung suspended and unmoving. Sections of the floor which had begun to push forward, and portions of wall which were falling inward, seemed frozen in space. Everyone was struggling over cracks and ducking beneath boulders poised to come crashing down upon them. Merlin continued his methodical pace, arms still moving, his face lined with strain and glistening with perspiration, still mumbling his incantation.

It seemed an eternity, but at last the dwarves, MacHinery, Maggie, and her two escorts reached the end of the tunnel and poured out into yet another cavern. Simon, still looking over his shoulder, joined them. Fearfully, they clustered together until Merlin appeared. He staggered slightly as he stepped from the tunnel, took several long paces forward, and with a moaning gasp, sank to his knees. Behind him there was a titanic crash as the tons of rock, released by the breaking of his counterspell, collapsed on all sides within the tunnel. A cloud of choking dust poured forth from what was left of the entrance and set them all coughing and gasping.

And at that moment, from the gloomy shadows of the cavern's ceiling, a vast shape hurled itself down upon them with an ear shattering roar and a rush of great wings. Blazing red eyes glared from a huge, horrible, scaled head, sword-length claws flexed, and a massive barbed tail lashed in fury. "Dragon!" shrieked a chorus of dwarf voices.

Caught completely by surprise, the army rallied as best it could. A score of arrows sped against the monster's scaled body, but bounced harmlessly off. With a single sweep of its clawed foreleg, the creature knocked a cluster of archers sprawling and lifeless. Its tail whipped in a great arc and slammed into another group of dwarves, hurling them, crushed and battered, in all directions. A half dozen brave axmen rushed in, swinging their weapons wildly against the huge head. Their axes simply shattered, and almost contemptuously, the monster smashed them with another blow of its foreleg. It snorted a jet of flame from its nostrils, turning yet another cluster of dwarves to shriveled, blackened hulks.

There was a sudden loud chattering sound as Sergeant Small pressed the trigger of his weapon and fired a full clip of bullets at the huge reptile. He aimed purposely high, and three of the bullets ripped into the dragon's great right eye, while a dozen more slammed into its hideous head. The creature gave a shriek of pain that reverberated through the cave, and gathered itself as though to spring. Its undamaged left eye, burning with rage, was fixed upon the figure of Merlin, still kneeling on the cavern floor.

Pointing his finger at the dragon's head, the wizard cried out a single word. With a sharp crack, a glaring bolt of lightning leaped through the air and struck the creature.

For a few moments there was total confusion. Momentarily blinded by the blazing bolt of lightning, and still coughing helplessly in the acrid smoke and dust that billowed about them, the dwarves stumbled and yelled in panic, expecting at any moment to have the dragon fall viciously upon them. Small was inserting a fresh ammunition clip into his weapon. Then they all heard the loud, monotone voice of the robot. "There is no further cause for alarm. The animal is lifeless."

Minutes passed before they could see again, for most of the torches had been dropped and extinguished. When his vision had cleared completely, Gwedhedda ordered new torches to be lit, and as they sprang to blazing life, everyone saw the immense bulk of the dragon lying sprawled and unmoving. Somewhat shakily, the Dwarf Chieftain walked to it, inspected it, then glanced about at the bodies of the dwarves. "Nearly a third of our number," he said, grimly. "And it would have wiped us out had you not been here, Merlin."

There was no answer.

Gwedhedda looked around quickly. The spot on which Merlin had been kneeling was vacant.

"Merlin!" he called, in a voice that broke with panic.

"He is gone," said Sir MacHinery.

"Gone? What do you mean?" asked Simon.

"The instant after he destroyed the animal with the electrical discharge, a group of demons appeared from a hidden opening. They bound his arms to his sides and stuffed a cloth into his mouth. He seemed too weak to resist them. They carried him off into an opening there." He pointed toward a section of the cavern wall. "It sealed behind them."

"Why didn't you go to his aid?" raged Gwedhedda.

The robot's twin scanning lenses stared into the dwarf's blazing eyes. "My orders are to seek out Urlug," he explained. "I can let nothing sway me from doing so."

"Och, och," wailed Maggie, with her hands clutching her head. "The demons have Great Merlin in their power. What shall we do?"

"Do?" said Simon. "We'll do what we came to do—what Merlin would want us to do. We'll keep going until we reach Urlug."

"We cannot go further without Merlin's magic to aid us," shouted Gwedhedda in a near fury.

"We have no choice, have we!" Simon answered in a voice that matched the dwarf's. "Did you expect an easy victory, Gwedhedda? A little walk through demonland, a skirmish or two, and then a feast to celebrate your conquest? This is a war, and in wars men often die or fall captive to the enemy. If you cannot face that fact, then take your dwarves and slink back to your city of Glamoreth. But we'll go on, with your help or without it."

"Losh," whispered Sergeant Small to Constable Wier. "I didna know he had this in him. What an officer he'd have made!"

Gwedhedda was staring in puzzlement at the physicist. He realized that Simon had suddenly taken command of the expedition, yet somehow this seemed fitting. Turning, he motioned to the four nearest torchbearers. "Forward," he said. "Two axemen with each of you." There were no archers left; all had been killed by the dragon. As the points of light moved off into the darkness, he turned back to confront Simon. "Dwarves do not slink away from battle," he said. "We will stay with you as long as there is one of us left to swing an ax."

"I felt sure that you would," replied Simon. Then, with the robot by his side, he strode after the torches flickering in the distance. Small, Wier, Angus, Maggie, and Bathsheba hurried to catch up to him. Whispering among themselves, the dwarves followed.

Chapter 18

Weakened as he was by the terrible strain of maintaining the counterspell to Urlug's earth shaking, followed by the need to use a word of power to destroy the dragon, Merlin was no match at all for the cluster of demons who swiftly engulfed him. A gag was shoved into his mouth so that he could not speak, and his arms and his fingertips were quickly wound tightly to his sides so that he could make no gesture. Deprived of the ability to speak an incantation or make a magical pass, and too weak to even struggle, he found himself picked up like a sack of potatoes and hustled into a small tunnel only a few feet from the one which had just collapsed.

The tunnel was pitch black, but the six demons knew their way and bore him swiftly along. Fatalistically, the wizard closed his eyes and gave himself up to his great weariness. In a short time, he actually fell asleep.

He was rudely awakened by being dropped upon a floor. He did not attempt to move, but opened his eyelids a tiny fraction to determine what sort of place he was in. Without moving his head, he was able to see that it was quite a large room, with floor, ceiling, and walls of polished black onyx. He lay at the foot of a massive gold throne. It was empty, but behind it stood of number of demons—high ranking nobles by their dress—who seemed to be silently waiting for something. The room was dimly illuminated by some source which he could not see. Suddenly, the throne was no longer empty. A shadow sat in it. A shadow in the shape of a man. The demons bowed.

"He is awake," said the shadow in a whisper like the sound of poisonous snakes hissing. "Remove the gag."

Clawed fingers fumbled at the base of his neck where the gag was tied, and the cloth was roughly yanked from his mouth. He opened his eyes fully and gazed up at the shadow. He was in no doubt as to what it was.

"Hail, Great Merlin," hissed the poisonous voice. "Hail, oh greatest of wizards, captured by a simple trick. It seems you are but another weak and ordinary mortal after all."

The demons behind the throne broke into grating laughter. "Hail, Urlug," replied Merlin calmly. Much of his strength had returned. "If I am but a weak and ordinary mortal, why do you deem it necessary to keep my hands tied so securely?"

"Oh, I know you have powers," countered the shadow, "and feeble though they are, I have no wish to become involved in a duel of magic with you." It leaned forward. "And now that I have you here, tell me, Great Merlin, who will be able to bear the Sword of Power against me?"

There was another chuckle, like the fluttering of bat wings, from the demons. Merlin immediately realized that he had a great advantage with which to work. As he had hoped, Urlug thought that he was to be the sword-bearer. He saw that he had an opportunity both to stall for more time for the army, and to keep Urlug from guessing who the real champion was.

So he threw his head back and gave a great, booming laugh which shocked the demons into surprised silence. "You are indeed a dunce, Urlug," he replied with obvious scorn. "Did you really think that I was to be the champion?"

"You cannot trick me, Merlin," hissed the shadow. "Who else could be?"

"Think, simpleton," sneered Merlin. "The champion must be fearless and unable to be tempted. I do not fear you, nor anything else, but if you knew anything of my past, you would know that I can be tricked. I was once unable to resist the guile of the witch woman, Nimue, and that is how I came to spend two thousand years as a prisoner beneath a lake. *I* could not have borne the sword against you—fool!"

He was deliberately trying to enrage the creature, and was pleased to see that he was succeeding. Two red sparks were kindling within its shadow face.

"Who carries the sword then?" demanded Urlug. "Tell me!"

"Oh, the sword is being *carried* by the mechanical slave," replied Merlin. "But when the time comes—and it will come, Urlug—the true champion will use it and then the world will be rid of another vermin."

Shrilly, the shadow voice screamed, "Who is the champion? You will tell me!"

Merlin chuckled. "You cannot take my mind," he said with calm confidence. "Our powers are too evenly matched."

"There are other ways," hissed the shadow.

Merlin chuckled again. "Torture? Do you think I cannot make myself immune to pain, simpleton? Do you think I cannot will myself to die, if need be?" He glanced at the demons behind the throne. "You poor fools. You have chosen a leader who fumbles about with guesses and who meets defeat at every turn. Was the army sent to overcome five mortals and three brownies at Maggie's cave not defeated by a means that he can not even explain? Has he been able to prevent our tiny army from continuing its advance against you despite your greater numbers? In the end he will be destroyed, and you will flee to your holes shrieking for mercy even as your ancestors did ages ago." The demons stared at him, their bulbous eyes glinting with fear.

"Silence!" The shadow uncoiled from the throne and stood upright, quivering with rage. "Do you think I cannot yet find the champion and tempt him aside or make him feel fear? Watch!"

It gestured with a shadowy arm. A circle of light appeared on the shiny black floor. Within it could be seen the army of dwarves, the shiny figure of the robot, Maggie, Simon, and the others. The shadow stared down at them.

"Gwedhedda," he said at last. "The Chieftain of the Dwarves. He is fearless; perhaps he is beyond temptation. We shall see. Watch now, Merlin, and see your champion fall to a lust that he does not even know lies within his mind."

The tiny remnant of the force moved gloomily through the darkness. The only sounds were the steady clank of the robot's metal feet rhythmically striking the stone floor, the labored breathing of the old witch, and the shuffling of the dwarves' leather boots. The faces of the dwarves were grim and purposeful, and the face of Gwedhedda seemed etched in stone. Simon's words had touched them to the quick, and they were avidly awaiting a chance to do battle with anything that stood in their way.

But the blow which Urlug now struck was a subtle one. The torches of the scouts, which had been moving steadily forward, suddenly stopped, wavered uncertainly, and then began to dart about.

"What is happening?" demanded Gwedhedda, tapping MacHinery on the arm.

"They have entered a cave," replied the robot. "They are in no trouble, but seem quite excited. They are rushing about, picking things up from the ground."

The dwarf frowned. "We'll see what it's all about," he grunted. "Follow me, dwarves, and have your weapons ready."

Cautiously, with the exception of Sir MacHinery who continued to clank methodically forward, the dwarves moved toward the dancing torches. And as they drew near enough to see within the cave, a great gasp went up.

The large floor of the cave was piled to the height of a man's knees with an immense and incredible horde of treasure. In the flickering firelight of the scouts' torches, thousands of bars of pure gold gleamed with an orange lustre, and ingots of shining silver glinted redly. There was a sparkling rainbow of brilliance from countless green glowing emeralds, flashing diamonds, pale pink topazes, deep blue sapphires, and sullen red rubies. There were hundreds of bars, lumps, and shards of semiprecious stones as well; deep yellow, translucent amber, jet black onyx, white-flecked, green jade, shining purple porphyry. And there were strange stones, never before seen by the eyes of man nor dwarf. Everywhere within the cave there were beckoning twinkles and gleamings and sparkles.

And the dwarves went mad.

Flinging aside their axes, they ran wildly into the cave, seizing first one sparkling gem or rare stone and then another; holding them up to see them gleam in the torch-light, trickling them through their fingers. They shouted at one another in loud, exulting voices.

His face impassive, Merlin watched this scene taking place within the circle of light, and knew that Urlug had contrived the cleverest of all methods for disposing of the dwarves. For dwarves are born with an insatiable love for the treasures of the earth—not because of a lust for wealth or greed of possession, but for the sheer love of beauty that can be created from such things by artistry and craftsmanship. The dwarf chieftain and his band had never seen such a vast assortment of treasures and they were hopelessly ensnared by them.

"There are tools here!" shouted one dwarf in a voice ringing with excitement. "Hammers and files and tongs. A brazier. A work table and a vice and tools for cutting gems."

The dwarves had found paradise. Their weapons were cast aside, their purpose forgotten. Simon shook Gwedhedda by the shoulder, but the dwarf did not even notice him. Looking into his glazed eyes, Simon saw it was useless. He glanced at MacHinery who was wading unconcernedly through the treasures toward the opposite end of the cave. "It's no use," he said grimly to Small and Wier and Maggie, who stood staring at the treasure and the maddened dwarves. "We've lost them. We'll have to go on without them." He hurried after the robot, and the others hurried after him. Wier prudently scooped up a handful of diamonds and tucked them into his uniform tunic pocket on his way out.

In the black onyx room Urlug exulted. "So much for Gwedhedda and his dwarves."

Merlin yawned, more for the effect it would have upon the watching demons than for Urlug's benefit. "Obviously, Gwedhedda was not the champion," he observed. "You were wrong again, Urlug. There are still four humans and a brownie left." He deliberately excluded mentioning MacHinery. "And they are continuing forward. Or had you not noticed?"

"That is easily seen to," said Urlug grimly.

Chapter 19

Old Angus, whose short legs made progress through the massive piles of treasure exceedingly difficult, waded and scrambled after the others as quickly as he could. They were some distance ahead of him when he finally reached the end of the cave, where he paused a moment to glower back at the dwarves. "Ye fools!" he shouted. "What will ye eat? How will ye live? Ye'll die here uselessly, workin' away at yer silly baubles. There'll be naught left o' ye in a few months but bare bones clutchin' handfuls o' bright stones!"

The dwarves did not even hear him. Some were excitedly heating up the brazier, others were gathering jewels and ingots of gold and silver. They babbled excitedly among themselves. Angus spat contemptuously into a pile of rubies worth a king's ransom and left the cave.

It was fortunate that his progress had been slow, and that he had stopped to jeer at the dwarves. For MacHinery, with Simon and the others having caught up with him, had moved on through a short tunnel and into another cave. They were clustered closely together, and the instant they entered, a mass of ropes dropped from the ceiling, covering them in a great net which immediately began to tighten. So thick were the ropes and so tightly did they entwine the group that MacHinery's arms were pinned to his sides. Angus, hurrying to catch up, found them like this, dimly visible in the faint glow from the treasure cave they had just left.

"Losh," exclaimed the brownie, and yanking his tiny dirk from its sheath in his stocking, began sawing at the rope.

"Cut the ones nearest MacHinery's right arm," grunted Simon. He was squeezed painfully between Small and Wier. Angus obeyed immediately. The ropes were as thick as his arm, but his dirk was razor sharp, and he was amazingly sturdy for his size. Even so, it was some time before the strands began to part and MacHinery was able to exert sufficient power with his hydraulic muscle to break the rope through. But this enabled him to free the arm that held the Sword of Power, and using this he began to cut through the remaining ropes with ease. Panting, Angus stopped sawing and sat down to watch. Within a short time, the robot had the entire group free.

At this very moment, from an opening at the other side of the cave, a dozen demon soldiers entered and immediately stopped, frozen in astonishment. They had expected to find the last members of the invading army trussed up tightly within a net of ropes, and had been ordered to drag them into the presence of Urlug and the chief demons. "I can take care o' these few," said Maggie, and pointing a gnarled finger at them, muttered a few words. One of the demons had been holding a torch which dropped suddenly to the ground, and in the light it cast they saw a dozen, large, black beetles which instantly scuttled from sight.

In the black room Urlug hissed like a snake. "That cursed witch and brownie." He seemed to ponder a moment. "Could it be the witch? She has minor powers and she seems to be without fear. I shall test her, and the brownie as well."

"Good luck," said Merlin, with a great deal more calmness in his voice that he actually felt. "Your last snare did not seem to work very well."

Urlug made no reply, but several of the demons were whispering agitatedly to one another, and the wizard saw a chance to heighten their obvious fear. "Your master seems ever more impotent, does he not? I tell you again, he will not stop the champion—nor can your entire army. I promise that you will see it melt away before your eyes."

"Silence!" exclaimed the shadow in a whispered shriek. It bent ferociously over the circle of light in which the figures of the four humans, the brownie, and the robot were revealed.

They were now moving through a pitch black tunnel, Simon in the lead, bearing the torch which the demon soldier had dropped. The tunnel was long, and it seemed to be taking hours for them to move through it. Maggie was gasping for breath. "We must stop a bit. I'm too old to keep goin' at such a pace."

"I fear I am too," agreed Angus, who was wheezing lustily.

Obediently, the robot stopped. "It is unfortunate that the aging process in humans causes such disabilities," he observed. "I have noted that your blood supply does not flow as well as in a younger individual. Thus, you tire more easily."

"Aye," sighed Maggie, " 'tis a mortal hard thing to grow old and not be able to walk as fast as ye'd like—or do many another thing ye could do when ye were young." She sighed again. "I've tried many a spell, as have most wizards and witches, but there seems no way to keep from gettin' old. Och, I'd dearly love to be young again."

"I too," agreed Angus.

Above the glowing circle, Urlug chuckled evilly. "That is the way," he hissed. "For both of them!"

After a time, Maggie indicated that she could continue once more, and the party resumed its progress. Only a few more minutes elapsed when they saw, far ahead, a faint light.

"What is it, MacHinery?" queried Simon.

"We are coming to another large cavern," explained the robot. "It seems to be lit by a torch. I find this unusual."

"So do I," grunted Angus. "Let me slip ahead and peer things oot. I'm small enough to keep from bein' seen."

"I'll come behind ye," said Sergeant Small, fondling his weapon. "Just in case it's a trap."

They moved cautiously, and as they neared the entrance to the cavern, Angus got down on all fours and crept stealthily forward. Carefully, he put his head around the corner and peered in. The cavern was small and was lit by a single torch, mounted in an iron wall bracket. From a crevice in one wall, a stream of water was trickling down into a large pool, formed by a semicircle of stones, some three feet high.

"A fountain," muttered the brownie, licking his lips.

The tiny leather water bottle he carried slung over one shoulder was nearly empty, and he had been feeling the pangs of thirst for some time. He turned and called to Small who was crouched some distance back in the tunnel. " 'Tis a small empty cavern lit by a torch, and there's a fountain in it. We can get a drink."

Small reported this to the others, who abandoned caution and came hurrying into the cavern.

"Och, I can sure use a drink!" exclaimed Constable Wier.

"Just a minute," said Simon. "It could be poisoned, put there to kill us all. MacHinery, can you detect any foreign substances in it?"

The robot marched to the pool and considered it. "It is nonpoisonous," he announced."

"Gude," said Angus, slipping his flask from his shoulder and unstoppering it. "Perchance this is but a place where the demons come fer their own water." But in the act of dipping his flask into the pool, a glint on the brown rock wall caught his eye. A golden plaque inscribed with Gaelic characters was inset into the rock. Squinting his eyes, the brownie read the words laboriously. "All who bathe herein will once again have the youth of their desire and the forgetting of their cares."

He translated this for the others, then spat contemptuously. "A bath! It may not be poison, but like as not 'tis some demon trick."

"I think you're right," observed Simon. "We'd best forget it. Let's keep going."

They had not taken more than a half dozen steps when Angus realized that Maggie was no longer with them. Turning, he saw her raptly gazing into the sparkling water of the pool. A sudden fear clutched his heart. "Nay, Maggie, nay," he said, hurrying back and tugging at her robe. " 'Tis a trick, I tell ye, a trick."

"Perhaps," said the witch in a sad voice. Then she smiled. "When I was a lass o' twenty, I was the prettiest girl in the Highlands. All the laddies sought me oot, but there was one I favored. His name was Ian. We used to walk in the woods, hand in hand."

"Wait, Maggie," yelped Angus, jumping up and down. "Dinna ye see this is a temptation for ye—and for me too, maybe. Like happened to the dwarves."

Suddenly, the witch plunged her hand into the water, then quickly withdrew it, regarding it almost fearfully. Droplets of water trickled off the rosy fingertips of the hand of a young girl. Slowly Maggie brought her other hand next to it; the withered, gnarled, age-spotted hand of an old woman beside the fresh, soft hand of a young girl.

"To be young again," whispered the old woman in a low, wondering voice. And suddenly, she stepped over the stone wall and plunged into the pool. With a wail of anguish, Bathsheba leaped in after her.

"Maggie!" shrieked Angus.

"Stop her," yelled Simon.

But it was too late. Tinkling laughter was their only answer. Simon, Small, Wier, and the brownie stood rooted to the floor in wonder as a figure stepped gracefully from the pool. Pulling back shining, golden hair that had been plastered wetly across her face, the girl gazed at them wonderingly out of clear, blue, young eyes. A tiny mewing from the pool caught her attention, and reaching back, she pulled a small, sodden kitten from the water.

"It worked!" said Angus wonderingly. "D'ye feel all right, Maggie?"

"It's hypnosis," said Simon, uncertainly.

"I feel wonderful," said the girl, answering the brownie's question, as she stroked the tiny kitten cradled in her arms. She glanced about the gloomy cavern. "But what am I doing in this awful place? I want to be out in the sunshine! I want to run through the grass!" With a happy laugh, she sped on twinkling feet back into the darkness of the tunnel through which they had just come.

"Maggie! Come back. We need ye!" shouted Constable Wier.

Angus shook his head. " 'Tis no use," he said wearily. "The plaque up there says that all cares will be forgotten. She doesna even remember why she's here." He gazed at the pool. "But it made her young again."

"Angus!" said Simon sharply. "Don't do it!"

The brownie looked up at him. "Dinna worry," he said, squaring his shoulders. "I'll not be tempted. I told Merlin I'd see this through to the end and do what had to be done. Let's be on our way."

In the room where Merlin lay bound, the shadow figure slowly reseated itself on the throne of gold. "So!" came the noxious whisper. "It is the brownie. He has shown no fear and he has resisted temptation. A good choice, Merlin, and one I little suspected. But I have found him out. He is too small to bear the sword, so you have the slave bearing it for him. No doubt you have a spell that will cause him to grow sufficiently at the proper moment."

"You assume too much," said Merlin, hurriedly. "There are still the three mortals. It could be one of them. Take care, least you make another mistake." He licked his lips, and there was a worried expression on his face.

"You poor fool," sneered the shadow, "you make it

more obvious every minute by your very protests. It is the brownie."

Inwardly, Merlin was laughing. Lo, I have become a skilled actor, he thought to himself. Should I ever lose my magic, I shall go upon the stage.

The shadow stood up. "The end is now in sight," it hissed softly. "Assemble the army!" The shadow bent forward, red eyes fixed upon the prostrate form of the wizard. "There is not even a need to waste further magic upon them. They will be slain by the spears and swords of my demons. I will even let you watch the death of your champion!" He laughed, and suddenly the shadow was gone and the spiraling, smoky thing that Merlin and Angus had seen days ago on the beach at Loch Bree, stood in its place. "Bring him!" it ordered, and swept out of the room.

Chapter

20

Saddened by the loss of the old witch, whom they had all come to love for her gentleness and wisdom, the three men and the brownie moved silently out of the torchlit cave and into another tunnel. They had walked only a short distance when Simon noticed something.

"This floor is smooth," he observed, peering downward. "It's not like the rest of the places we've been through."

" 'Tis like a road," remarked Constable Wier.

"Unless I miss my guess," said Angus grimly, " 'tis the beginnin' o' the road that leads to the city o' the demons."

Each man felt his heart begin to pound with excitement. Sergeant Small checked his Sten gun and adjusted his canvas bag to a more convenient position. Wier clutched his nightstick tightly. As a weapon it was quite ineffective, but it was, to him, a symbol of his authority as a British constable.

Rounding a bend, they suddenly came to the tunnel's end. The road widened into a broad, flat highway. And ranged across it, less than fifty yards away, drawn up in battle array, was the army of Demonland.

There were several thousand of them, Simon guessed. The foot soldiers in their dull black, scale armor, holding iron shields and armed with cruelly barbed spears, were drawn up in two groups. They stood beneath colored banners of blood red and jet black that hung limply in the windless air. In the center of the array was the host of demon cavalry, dressed in black and silver armor and helmets ringed with sharp pointed horns. They carried curved swords and long lances, and were mounted upon giant, red-eyed rats which were also sheathed in black and silver armor, and hung with tasseled trappings of red.

There was a brief moment of silence as the immense horde of demons and the tiny handful of invaders from the upper world regarded one another. Then, clearing his throat, Constable Jock Wier took three steps forward and pointed his wooden nightstick at the demon army.

"I arrest ye in the name o' Her Majesty's government," he announced in a loud voice, "for disturbin' the peace and incitin' a riot. I warn you that anything ye say may be used in evidence against ye. Noo, lay doon yer weapons and come along peaceable."

The spectacle of a single policeman attempting to arrest this entire weird army was so ludicrous that Simon couldn't hold back a nervous giggle. For a moment he wondered wildly where Wier would find a jail big enough to hold them all.

"Nice try, Jock," grunted Sergeant Major Small, "but it's no gude. They're goin' to charge. Lie doon, all o' ye."

Dipping his hand into the canvas bag, he brought out a grenade, yanked the pin, and threw it in a high arc that brought it down right at the front of the charging demon cavalry. There was a burst of flame and an explosion that roared with tremendous violence throughout the cavern. A half dozen rats and riders went down squealing and shrieking in pain. Without waiting a moment, Small hurled another grenade after the first. The charge shuddered to a stop as the rats, overcome with fear and out of control of their riders, scattered in all directions.

"So much for them," chuckled Small. "Noo for the infantry." Dropping to one knee, he began to fire short bursts from the Sten gun into the ranks of the demons who were milling about uncertainly, still terrified at the noise and disaster caused by the grenades. The Sten gun also made a tremendous racket, and there were screams of pain as dozens of the horrid creatures were felled by its bullets. The demons understood swords and spears and axes, but these terrible noises and flashes of light and invisible death that struck them down were powerful magic against which they were helpless. Their front ranks began to press back against the rear ones in terror. The nobles who led them were in as great a panic as their troops.

"They'll break in a minute," observed Small, professionally. He fished out his last grenade, pulled its pin, and threw it so that it fell into the center of a mass of demons. There was another terrible explosion, and more screams of pain and terror.

"Remember what I told you, Lords of Demonland," boomed a loud and familiar voice from somewhere behind the demon army. "You cannot withstand us. Urlug is powerless to aid you. You will be swept away likes leaves in a wind."

"That's Merlin!" yelled Simon in wild exuberance.

The demons broke. Flinging down their spears, they fled in terror along the road toward their city, fighting and jostling one another to escape. Almost in seconds, the road was empty save for two figures. One was Merlin, hands still tightly bound to his sides. The other was Urlug, writhing and curling in rage, his red eyes aglow with hatred.

"Your great army seems to have been defeated," commented Merlin.

"They will be suitably punished," Urlug hissed like an angry serpent. "But I need them not. Behold! Your champion is now my captive."

Angus suddenly found himself enclosed in a small, closely barred cage. "What's this?" he yelped in dismay.

But MacHinery was still moving swiftly forward. In the light of the torches, which had been thrown aside by the fleeing demons and lay smouldering on the road, the great sword glinted in his hands. "Wrong again, Urlug," said Merlin. "My champion is now coming to put an end to you, foul creature of darkness!"

Urlug coiled backward in dismay, perceiving suddenly that he had been tricked. Until this moment, as Merlin had so desperately hoped, Urlug had regarded the robot as a mindless mechanical slave. It had been more than a thousand years since he had last been called to the upper world, and when he thought of machines at all it was only in terms of things that moved by means of cogs and wheels or counterweights—like a drawbridge or a watermill. He was baffled by this silvery, manlike creature, but as yet, he had no fear of it. Summoning his power, he engulfed the robot in a blast of flame that would have burnt any living creature to a crisp, and turned lead or even iron into molten, running liquid.

MacHinery continued to move forward, unharmed. The metal alloy from which he was constructed could withstand temperatures far hotter than ordinary fire. Rapidly the distance between the small, silver figure and the great, smoky one was closing.

"You cannot destroy him," said Merlin, calmly. "And he is without fear."

"Hold!" hissed Urlug to the robot. "What do you want? Wealth? Power? I can give it to you!"

Merlin laughed, and MacHinery gave no answer, for Urlug's words meant nothing to him. He was a machine, about to perform his function. The great sword swung up and back, ready for the single, final blow.

And Urlug realized that he could tempt this creature no more than he could have tempted a drawbridge or a watermill. He realized that it was without fear, and that he could not destroy it. It was the perfect champion. Had he known this earlier, he might have devised some way of overcoming it, but it was too late.

So Urlug fled! He fled in terror from the Sword of Power in the hands of the champion who could end his existence. And as he fled, MacHinery gave chase.

"Come on," yelled Simon, rushing after him. Wier paused to grab up a burning torch, Small yelled in triumph, and they joined the chase. With Urlug's hold on him gone, Merlin muttered a spell, and the ropes that entwined him fell away. He dashed after the others.

They passed down the broad highway and into city of the demons. From the openings that led into their dwelling places, demons peered with luminescent, fear-filled eyes. They watched their once powerful ally fleeing in fear before the small, silver bearer of the sword and the mortals from upper earth.

They passed out of the city and into a lightless cavern of brown granite, down one wall of which poured a gushing waterfall which plunged noisily into a broad, underground river. Following the river's bank, Urlug sped into a long tunnel of stygian blackness, through a cavern of greenish rock, and into another cavern of brown granite. The path he took led downward, toward the very depths of earth. Steps behind him, clanked the robot with upraised sword, and at a distance came the four men, following his progress by the glimmer of the torchlight on his silver body.

At last, they entered an immense, gloomy cavern filled with gigantic and fantastically shaped lumps of black basalt, among which Urlug whirled and dodged, with the robot just steps behind. The entire cavern sloped down like a bowl, and at its very bottom was a circular patch which, even to MacHinery's vision, appeared pure black. This was the gateway to the region from which he had come, and it was to it now that Urlug fled in desperation. Sir MacHinery was less than twenty paces behind him.

But suddenly, with one foot raised in midair, the robot stopped dead. Then gently, the silver figure collapsed to the ground with a faint clatter. Its hands relaxed.

Simon, with Small and Wier right behind him, saw what had happened. They were panting for breath from the chase, but Simon shrieked, "MacHinery!" and with a burst of speed reached the sprawled figure. He knelt beside it, and almost absentmindedly picked up the sword which had fallen from the robot's hand.

"What's happened," gasped Wier, catching up to him.

"Some kind of malfunction," said Simon desperately. "A short circuit, a wire jerked loose, heaven knows what. But he's out of commission."

At the brink of the pit of blackness, the shape of Urlug paused, taking in the scene. The four men heard a sudden horrible hissing of laughter, and looking up, saw the great smokelike figure rolling toward them.

"Victory is mine after all," it gloated. "A mere machine cannot defeat me. With my magic I have destroyed it!"

Simon exploded in fury. He knew that MacHinery's malfunction was purely mechanical. For Urlug to claim that it was the result of any supernatural effort made the physicist nearly dance with rage.

"Curse you, Urlug!" he shouted. "Your so-called magic had nothing to do with this! I'm sick and tired of all this mystical, magical nonsense. There's a logical explanation for everything that's happened and I'm going to figure it out. I don't believe in your infernal magic or any other kind."

As Simon made this statement, he angrily swung the sword in a ferocious arc. It sliced into Urlug's smoky body.

And Urlug was gone. He simply blinked out of existence, like a flashlight beam that has been turned off. Simon was left standing, poised on the balls of his feet, with the sword pointing straight out ahead of him into the blackness of the cavern.

"Ye did him in!" exclaimed Small, in a voice that trembled with awe and jubilation.

"Frankly, I think he did himself in," said the physicist, shortly. "He believed that this sword could destroy him, so it did. There's nothing supernatural about it. African witch doctors can make people die just by telling them they've been hexed. That's what's at the bottom of all superstition and magic—belief, instead of knowledge."

Merlin gazed at the excited young scientist. In those clothes, armed with the sword, and with his hair and beard trimmed that way, he is the image of King Arthur, thought the magician. The prophecies were true—Arthur and Merlin were together again when the world needed them!

Aloud he said, "Simon—an age has ended. I can feel it. I think the very strength of your disbelief has put an end to all magic. He pointed at a rock and muttered a charm. Nothing happened. "Yes," he sighed, "It's as I feared. I tried to call that pebble to me, but my magic is gone. Perhaps it's just as well, for neither Urlug nor I really belong in this world of yours. The time of magic has passed."

Simon stared at him. "I'm sorry, Merlin," he mumbled.

The magician held up a hand. "No matter," he said. "We have other things to worry about, anyway."

Turning, Simon trudged back to the immobile figure of Sir MacHinery. "Can ye fix him?" asked Wier hopefully. "Or is he—dead, like?"

"I can fix him," said Simon confidently. He looked at Merlin. "You're still in command. We've got to get out of here. What's next?"

"Many things," stated the wizard. "We have a small,

brave brownie who must be released from a cage, a young maiden and a kitten who are no doubt wandering about in these caverns and must be found, a group of ensnared dwarves who must be persuaded to return to their home, a blocked tunnel that has to be opened somehow, a long climb upstairs that I look forward to with little relish, and then"—he grinned—"at least two weeks of conversation which you have promised me."

Simon grinned back and, handing him the sword, took hold of MacHinery beneath the metal arms. Wier hastened to take the robot's feet, and the four men, with Small leading the way and Merlin bringing up the rear, began their journey out of darkness and danger, toward the bright sunlight, and a world which, all unknowing, had one less problem to worry about.

Merlin lagged behind the others until he was sure they were paying no attention to him. He glanced about until he saw a small boulder lying a few yards away on the rocky floor. Pointing a finger at it, he muttered something. The boulder sailed through the air and landed gently in the palm of his hand where it turned immediately into a heavy, saw-toothed steel file.

"We'll need this to free Angus from his cage," chuckled Merlin, "since I no longer have any magical power!" He slid the file into the sleeve of his robe and, whistling a gay, sixth-century tune, hurried to catch up to the others.

Tom McGowen is a writer, artist, and editor. Among his books are *Hammet and the Highlanders* and his picture books, *Apple Strudel Soldier* and *Dragon Stew*.

Mr. McGowen has always lived in the Chicago area, where he attended Roosevelt University and The American Academy of Art. He lives with his wife and four children in Norridge, Illinois.

Trina Schart Hyman attended the art schools of the Philadelphia and Boston museums, as well as one in Stockholm, Sweden. She has illustrated many children's books, including *Epaminondas* by Eve Merriam and *Dragon Stew* by Tom McGowen.

She and her daughter live in a two-hundred-year-old stone house located on the banks of the Connecticut River in rural New Hampshire. Mrs. Hyman enjoys gardening, canoeing, and bicycling.